NATIONAL GEOGRAPHIC
Reach for Reading™

COMMON CORE PROGRAM

NATIONAL
GEOGRAPHIC

Hampton-Brown

Acknowledgments
Grateful acknowledgment is given to the authors, artists, photographers, museums, publishers, and agents for permission to reprint copyrighted material. Every effort has been made to secure the appropriate permission. If any omissions have been made or if corrections are required, please contact the Publisher.

Cover Illustration: Joel Sotelo

Illustration Credits: 5, 51, 71, and 86 Illustrations by Cindy Davis; 37 National Geographic / Cengage legacy illustrations

Photographic Credits: 12 (cr) National Archives and Records Administration; 16 (tr) DigitalStock/Corbis; 43 (cr) Gillie Newman/Getty Images; 70(tr) Corel.

Visit National Geographic Learning online at www.NGSP.com

Visit our corporate website at www.cengage.com

Printed in the USA.

Printer: RR Donnelley, Harrisonburg, VA

ISBN: 978-12850-38025

12 13 14 15 16 17 18 19 20 21

10 9 8 7 6 5 4 3 2 1

Benchmark Assessments
Contents at a Glance

Assessments Overview
Multiple Measures to Assess Student Learning

National Geographic *Reach for Reading* is a Common Core reading program that reaches all students and empowers every classroom to reach for reading success. *Reach for Reading* offers a comprehensive array of assessments and tools to

- monitor student progress and inform instruction throughout the year
- encourage students to participate in their learning
- document student progress on Common Core State Standards.

In each unit, there is a variety of assessments and tools you can use to monitor student progress on a weekly and unit level.

Weekly Tests	Unit Tests
Reading Comprehension	Reading Comprehension
Vocabulary	Vocabulary
Writing, Revising, and Editing	Writing, Revising, and Editing
Spelling	Oral Reading
Reading Strategies	

Additional assessments and tools can be used periodically throughout the program:

- Reteaching Masters for Weekly and Unit Tests
- Speaking and Listening Observation Log
- Test-Taking Strategies
- Comprehension Coach
- Benchmark Assessments
- Affective and Metacognitive Measures

Benchmark Assessments

Description and Purpose

The Benchmark Assessments are designed to measure student progress on grade-level Common Core State Standards to inform instruction and help ensure student success.

For each grade, there are three forms of Benchmark Tests — Form A, Form B, and Form C. Each form includes a Reading Test and a Writing Test. Each form of the Benchmark Tests assesses approximately the same grade-level Common Core State Standards, but with different reading material and test items so that students encounter new content each time they take a different form of the Benchmark Test.

Each test includes both multiple-choice items as well as items requiring student-generated responses that are scored using rubrics.

Benchmark Tests may be administered periodically throughout the year, such as at the beginning, middle, and end of the school year. Because all forms cover approximately the same Common Core State Standards, the Benchmark Tests help you monitor student progress on grade-level standards at key points throughout the school year.

The Benchmark Assessments are available in the following formats:

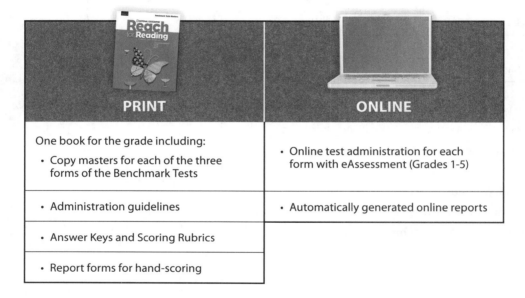

PRINT	ONLINE
One book for the grade including: • Copy masters for each of the three forms of the Benchmark Tests	• Online test administration for each form with eAssessment (Grades 1-5)
• Administration guidelines	• Automatically generated online reports
• Answer Keys and Scoring Rubrics	
• Report forms for hand-scoring	

Scheduling the Benchmark Tests

The Benchmark Assessments are not timed, so you have the flexibility to lengthen or shorten the testing times based on the needs of your students. You may also split testing into two sessions.

The Benchmark Reading Test for each form includes about 50 items (multiple-choice and constructed-response items). To avoid student fatigue, you may wish to administer the test in two sessions. If so, end the first session before students begin the fourth reading passage.

The Benchmark Writing Test for each form includes 16 items (12 multiple-choice items and 4 writing prompts). To avoid student fatigue, you may wish to administer the test in two sessions. If so, end the first session after Item 13.

The following chart shows the approximate administration times for each Benchmark Test. Since the tests are not timed, you may vary the administration time based on your students' needs.

Benchmark Assessments Administration Times				
Test	Session 1	Approximate Time	Session 2	Approximate Time
Reading	Items 1-25	45 minutes	Items 26-50	45 minutes
Writing	Items 1-13	45 minutes	Items 14-16	45 minutes

Administering the Benchmark Tests

Choose the form of the Benchmark Test that you will administer to your class. You might choose to use Form A at the beginning of the year, Form B in the middle of the year, and Form C near the end of the year. The Reading Test and the Writing Test should be administered on different days given the amount of time it will take for the students to complete each test. See the divider page that precedes each test for additional guidelines for test administration.

■ If students will be taking the tests online, follow the directions in eAssessment to assign the test.

■ If you are using the copy masters from this book:

- Make one copy of the test for each student.

- Read over the test that you will be administering so that you are familiar with the directions and are prepared for any questions students might ask.

- Distribute one copy of the test to each student. Have the students write their name and the date on the test.

- Make sure that students have additional paper to respond to test questions that require a student-written response.

- Explain that the Benchmark Test will help you and the students know more about which Common Core State Standards for their grade they already know, and which ones they need to work on.

When administering the Benchmark Test early in the year, it is important for students to know that some of the Standards may not have been taught yet, so they should not be discouraged if they do not know all the answers. Explain that there will be other opportunities, later in the school year, to show their progress on the Common Core State Standards.

- If students have questions about the directions, you may paraphrase as necessary to make sure the students understand what to do.

- Tell the students the approximate amount of time they will have to complete their test.

- If you are administering the test in two sessions, collect the tests at the end of the first session. When you are ready to begin the second session, return students' tests, and let them know the approximate amount of time they will have to complete the test.

- Collect the test for hand-scoring.

Scoring and Reporting Benchmark Test Results
Answer Keys and Rubrics

■ For eAssessment administration: Score the constructed-response items using the PDFs of the rubrics that are provided online. Then, follow the directions in eAssessment to record these scores.

Once students' scores are entered, eAssessment will generate online reports for the students in your class.

■ For print administration: Use the Answer Keys and Rubrics to score the students' tests. Each form of the test has two pages of Answer Keys and Rubrics to score student responses. The Answer Key also includes the Common Core State Standard codes for each item.

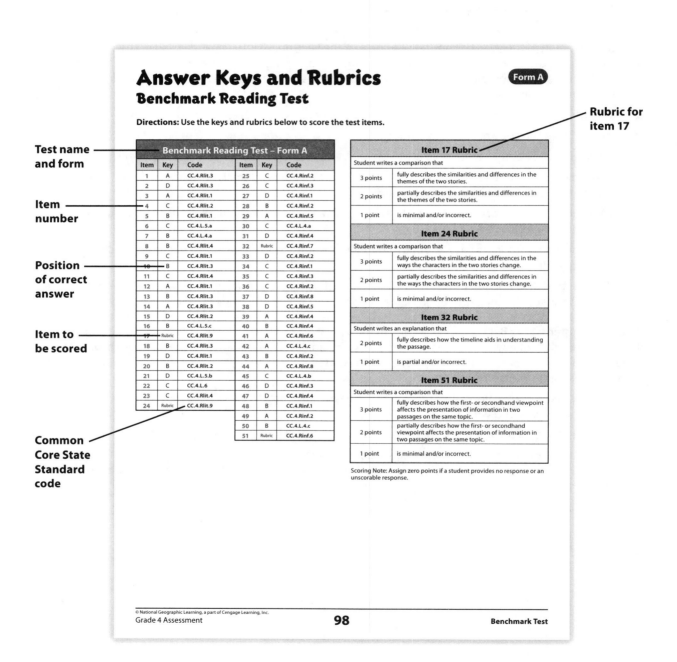

Test name and form

Item number

Position of correct answer

Item to be scored

Common Core State Standard code

Rubric for item 17

Answer Keys and Rubrics
Benchmark Reading Test

Form A

Directions: Use the keys and rubrics below to score the test items.

Benchmark Reading Test – Form A

Item	Key	Code	Item	Key	Code
1	A	CC.4.Rlit.3	25	C	CC.4.Rinf.2
2	D	CC.4.Rlit.3	26	C	CC.4.Rinf.3
3	A	CC.4.Rlit.1	27	D	CC.4.Rinf.1
4	C	CC.4.Rlit.2	28	B	CC.4.Rinf.2
5	B	CC.4.Rlit.1	29	A	CC.4.Rinf.5
6	C	CC.4.L.5.a	30	C	CC.4.L.4.a
7	B	CC.4.L.4.a	31	D	CC.4.Rinf.4
8	B	CC.4.Rlit.4	32	Rubric	CC.4.Rinf.7
9	C	CC.4.Rlit.1	33	D	CC.4.Rinf.2
10	B	CC.4.Rlit.3	34	C	CC.4.Rinf.1
11	C	CC.4.Rlit.4	35	C	CC.4.Rinf.3
12	A	CC.4.Rlit.1	36	C	CC.4.Rinf.2
13	B	CC.4.Rlit.3	37	D	CC.4.Rinf.8
14	A	CC.4.Rlit.3	38	D	CC.4.Rinf.5
15	D	CC.4.Rlit.2	39	A	CC.4.Rinf.4
16	B	CC.4.L.5.c	40	B	CC.4.Rinf.4
17	Rubric	CC.4.Rlit.9	41	A	CC.4.Rinf.6
18	B	CC.4.Rlit.3	42	A	CC.4.L.4.c
19	D	CC.4.Rlit.1	43	B	CC.4.Rinf.2
20	B	CC.4.Rlit.2	44	A	CC.4.Rinf.8
21	D	CC.4.L.5.b	45	C	CC.4.L.4.b
22	C	CC.4.L.6	46	D	CC.4.Rinf.3
23	C	CC.4.Rlit.4	47	D	CC.4.Rinf.4
24	Rubric	CC.4.Rlit.9	48	B	CC.4.Rinf.1
			49	A	CC.4.Rinf.2
			50	B	CC.4.L.4.c
			51	Rubric	CC.4.Rinf.6

Item 17 Rubric

Student writes a comparison that

3 points	fully describes the similarities and differences in the themes of the two stories.
2 points	partially describes the similarities and differences in the themes of the two stories.
1 point	is minimal and/or incorrect.

Item 24 Rubric

Student writes a comparison that

3 points	fully describes the similarities and differences in the ways the characters in the two stories change.
2 points	partially describes the similarities and differences in the ways the characters in the two stories change.
1 point	is minimal and/or incorrect.

Item 32 Rubric

Student writes an explanation that

2 points	fully describes how the timeline aids in understanding the passage.
1 point	is partial and/or incorrect.

Item 51 Rubric

Student writes a comparison that

3 points	fully describes how the first- or secondhand viewpoint affects the presentation of information in two passages on the same topic.
2 points	partially describes how the first- or secondhand viewpoint affects the presentation of information in two passages on the same topic.
1 point	is minimal and/or incorrect.

Scoring Note: Assign zero points if a student provides no response or an unscorable response.

Grade 4 Assessment · 98 · Benchmark Test

Writing Traits Rubric

The Writing Traits Rubric is an analytic scoring tool you can use to evaluate various types of student writing based on traits of good writing. Use this rubric to score the student responses for items 14-16 in the Benchmark Writing Tests.

© National Geographic Learning, a part of Cengage Learning, Inc.
Grade 4 Assessment

Writing Traits Rubric

Score Point	Topic and Support	Organization	Voice	Word Choice	Sentence Fluency	Conventions
4	• The writing has a clear topic and focused message that keeps readers interested. • Details are accurate and relevant, showing in-depth knowledge of the topic.	• The writing has a clear structure throughout that suits the writer's audience and purpose. • All content flows smoothly and logically.	• The writing sounds genuine and unique. • The writer's tone is appropriate to the purpose and audience.	• Effective words were chosen to clearly convey the writer's message. • Language used throughout is appropriate for the audience and grabs readers' attention.	• All sentences are varied and effective and have appropriate transitions. • When read aloud, the writing sounds natural and rhythmic.	• The writing has no more than a few minor errors in spelling, punctuation, capitalization, grammar, usage, and paragraphing. • All the sentences are complete.
3	• The writing has an adequate topic and message that keeps readers interested. • Most details are accurate and relevant, showing reasonable knowledge of the topic.	• The writing has an adequate structure that suits the writer's audience and purpose. • Most of the content flows smoothly and logically.	• Most of the writing sounds genuine and unique. • The writer's tone is mostly appropriate for the purpose and audience.	• Many appropriate words were chosen to clearly convey the writer's message. • Most language is appropriate for the audience and grabs readers' attention.	• Most sentences are varied and effective and have appropriate transitions. • When read aloud, most of the writing sounds natural and rhythmic.	• The writing has some errors in spelling, punctuation, capitalization, grammar, usage, and paragraphing. • Most of the sentences are complete.
2	• The writing has a somewhat unclear and unfocused topic and message, causing readers some confusion. • Some details are relevant and accurate, showing minimal knowledge of the topic.	• The writing has a vague structure that may suit the writer's audience and purpose. • Some content flows smoothly and logically.	• Some of the writing sounds genuine and unique. • The writer's tone is somewhat inappropriate for the purpose and audience.	• Some appropriate words were chosen to convey the writer's message. • Some language is appropriate for the audience and grabs readers' attention.	• Some sentences are varied and effective and have appropriate transitions. • When read aloud, some of the writing sounds natural and rhythmic.	• The writing has enough errors in spelling, punctuation, capitalization, grammar, usage, and paragraphing to necessitate rereading. • Some of the sentences are complete.
1	• The writing does not have a clear, focused topic or message, causing readers confusion. • Many details are irrelevant and/or inaccurate, indicating a lack of knowledge of the topic.	• The writing does not have a structure. • The content does not flow smoothly or logically.	• The writing does not sound genuine or unique. • The writer's tone is not appropriate for the purpose or audience.	• Few appropriate words were chosen to convey the writer's message. • Language is dull, vague, and inappropriate for the audience, losing the readers' attention.	• Few or none of the sentences are varied or effective or have appropriate transitions. • When read aloud, the writing sounds unnatural.	• The writing has many errors in spelling, punctuation, capitalization, grammar, usage, and paragraphing, impeding understanding. • Few sentences are complete.
0	Assign a score of zero for no response or an unscorable response.					

Student Profiles

Use the Student Profiles to record student scores and report results. There are two Student Profiles, one for all three forms of the Benchmark Reading Tests and another for all forms of the Benchmark Writing Tests. The Student Profile includes the grade-level Common Core State Standards codes and text for easy reference, and shows the items in the tests that are aligned with each standard.

Benchmark Reading Tests Student Profile

Circle item number for each correct item

Rubric score for handwritten response

Subtotal

Total score for the test

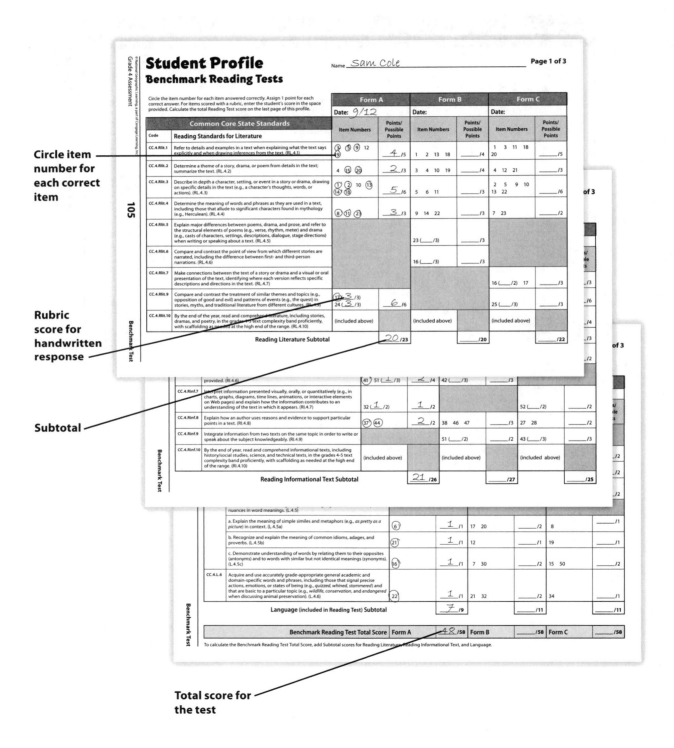

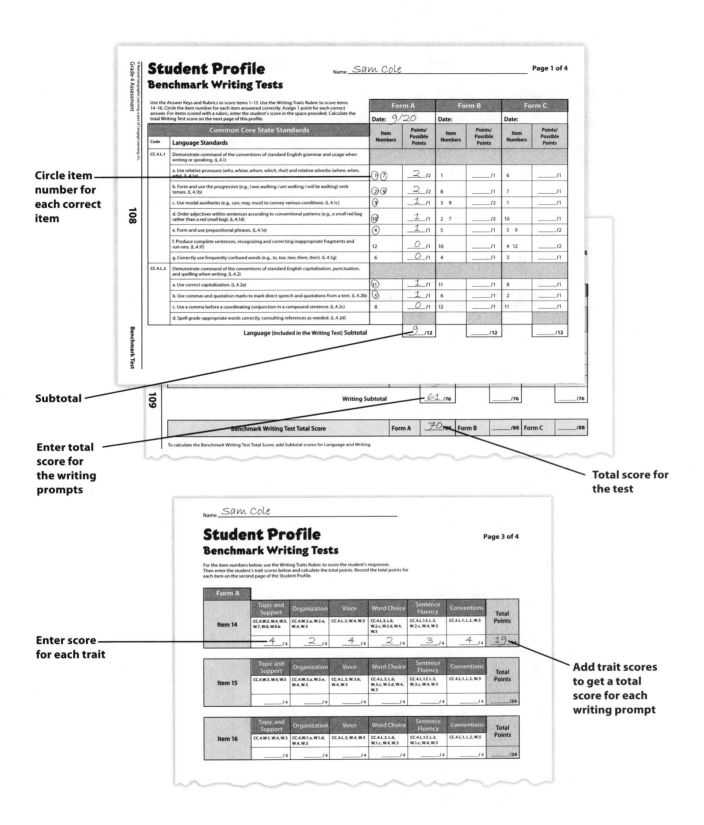

Circle item number for each correct item

Subtotal

Enter total score for the writing prompts

Total score for the test

Enter score for each trait

Add trait scores to get a total score for each writing prompt

Student Profile
Benchmark Writing Tests

Name: Sam Cole   Page 1 of 4

Use the Answer Keys and Rubrics to score items 1–13. Use the Writing Traits Rubric to score items 14–16. Circle the item number for each item answered correctly. Assign 1 point for each correct answer. For items scored with a rubric, enter the student's score in the space provided. Calculate the total Writing Test score on the next page of this profile.

© National Geographic Learning a part of Cengage Learning, Inc.
Grade 4 Assessment

108

Benchmark Test

Common Core State Standards		Form A		Form B		Form C	
		Date: 9/20		Date:		Date:	
Code	Language Standards	Item Numbers	Points/ Possible Points	Item Numbers	Points/ Possible Points	Item Numbers	Points/ Possible Points
CC.4.L.1	Demonstrate command of the conventions of standard English grammar and usage when writing or speaking. (L.4.1)						
	a. Use relative pronouns (who, whose, whom, which, that) and relative adverbs (where, when, why). (L.4.1a)	①⑦	2/2	1	/1	6	/1
	b. Form and use the progressive (e.g., I was walking; I am walking; I will be walking) verb tenses. (L.4.1b)	②⑨	2/2	8	/1	7	/1
	c. Use modal auxiliaries (e.g., can, may, must) to convey various conditions. (L.4.1c)	③	1/1	3 9	/2	1	/1
	d. Order adjectives within sentences according to conventional patterns (e.g., a small red bag rather than a red small bag). (L.4.1d)	⑩	1/1	2 7	/2	10	/1
	e. Form and use prepositional phrases. (L.4.1e)	④	1/1	5	/1	5 9	/2
	f. Produce complete sentences, recognizing and correcting inappropriate fragments and run-ons. (L.4.1f)	12	0/1	10	/1	4 12	/2
	g. Correctly use frequently confused words (e.g., to, too, two; there, their). (L.4.1g)	6	0/1	4	/1	3	/1
CC.4.L.2	Demonstrate command of the conventions of standard English capitalization, punctuation, and spelling when writing. (L.4.2)						
	a. Use correct capitalization. (L.4.2a)	⑪	1/1	11	/1	8	/1
	b. Use commas and quotation marks to mark direct speech and quotations from a text. (L.4.2b)	⑤	1/1	6	/1	2	/1
	c. Use a comma before a coordinating conjunction in a compound sentence. (L.4.2c)	8	0/1	12	/1	11	/1
	d. Spell grade-appropriate words correctly, consulting references as needed. (L.4.2d)						
	Language (included in the Writing Test) Subtotal		9/12		/12		/12

109

	Form A		Form B		Form C	
Writing Subtotal	61/76		/76		/76	

Benchmark Writing Test Total Score	Form A	70/88	Form B	/88	Form C	/88

To calculate the Benchmark Writing Test Total Score, add Subtotal scores for Language and Writing.

Name: Sam Cole

Student Profile
Benchmark Writing Tests

Page 3 of 4

For the item numbers below, use the Writing Traits Rubric to score the student's responses. Then enter the student's trait scores below and calculate the total points. Record the total points for each item on the second page of the Student Profile.

Form A

	Topic and Support	Organization	Voice	Word Choice	Sentence Fluency	Conventions	Total Points
Item 14	CC.4.W.2, W.4, W.5, W.7, W.8, W.9.b	CC.4.W.2.a, W.2.e, W.4, W.5	CC.4.L.3, W.4, W.5	CC.4.L.3, L.6, W.2.c, W.2.d, W.4, W.5	CC.4.L.1.f, L.3, W.2.c, W.4, W.5	CC.4.L.1, L.2, W.5	
	4/4	2/4	4/4	2/4	3/4	4/4	19/24

	Topic and Support	Organization	Voice	Word Choice	Sentence Fluency	Conventions	Total Points
Item 15	CC.4.W.3, W.4, W.5	CC.4.W.3.a, W.3.e, W.4, W.5	CC.4.L.3, W.3.b, W.4, W.5	CC.4.L.3, L.6, W.3.c, W.3.d, W.4, W.5	CC.4.L.1.f, L.3, W.3.c, W.4, W.5	CC.4.L.1, L.2, W.5	
	/4	/4	/4	/4	/4	/4	/24

	Topic and Support	Organization	Voice	Word Choice	Sentence Fluency	Conventions	Total Points
Item 16	CC.4.W.1, W.4, W.5	CC.4.W.1.a, W.1.d, W.4, W.5	CC.4.L.3, W.4, W.5	CC.4.L.3, L.6, W.1.c, W.4, W.5	CC.4.L.1.f, L.3, W.1.c, W.4, W.5	CC.4.L.1, L.2, W.5	
	/4	/4	/4	/4	/4	/4	/24

Using Test Results

Use the results for the Benchmark Tests to monitor student progress on grade-level Common Core State Standards. Since the results are organized by standard, you can quickly determine which students need more instruction or additional practice in a specific standard to help you plan instruction.

Having the results of multiple administrations included on the Student Profile not only allows you to see which students still need additional instruction and practice, but it also shows at a glance which students have made progress on Common Core State Standards from one administration to the next.

Class Grouping Summary

Use the Class Grouping Summary to record the names or initials of students who would benefit from more instruction or practice on tasks related to each Common Core State Standard.

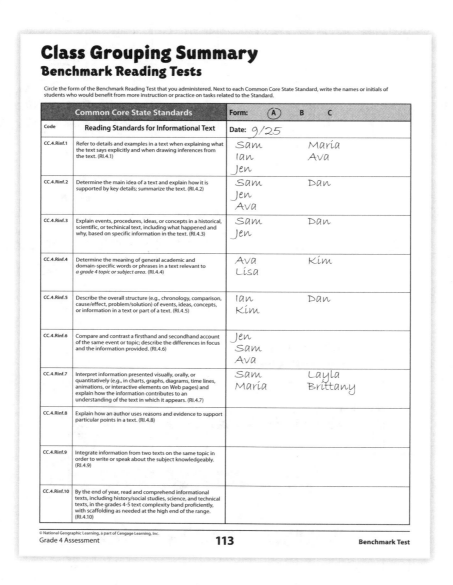

Class Grouping Summary
Benchmark Reading Tests

Circle the form of the Benchmark Reading Test that you administered. Next to each Common Core State Standard, write the names or initials of students who would benefit from more instruction or practice on tasks related to the Standard.

Common Core State Standards		Form: (A) B C
Code	**Reading Standards for Informational Text**	Date: 9/25
CC.4.Rinf.1	Refer to details and examples in a text when explaining what the text says explicitly and when drawing inferences from the text. (RI.4.1)	Sam Maria Ian Ava Jen
CC.4.Rinf.2	Determine the main idea of a text and explain how it is supported by key details; summarize the text. (RI.4.2)	Sam Dan Jen Ava
CC.4.Rinf.3	Explain events, procedures, ideas, or concepts in a historical, scientific, or techinical text, including what happened and why, based on specific information in the text. (RI.4.3)	Sam Dan Jen
CC.4.Rinf.4	Determine the meaning of general academic and domain-specific words or phrases in a text relevant to a grade 4 topic or subject area. (RI.4.4)	Ava Kim Lisa
CC.4.Rinf.5	Describe the overall structure (e.g., chronology, comparison, cause/effect, problem/solution) of events, ideas, concepts, or information in a text or part of a text. (RI.4.5)	Ian Dan Kim
CC.4.Rinf.6	Compare and contrast a firsthand and secondhand account of the same event or topic; describe the differences in focus and the information provided. (RI.4.6)	Jen Sam Ava
CC.4.Rinf.7	Interpret information presented visually, orally, or quantitatively (e.g., in charts, graphs, diagrams, time lines, animations, or interactive elements on Web pages) and explain how the information contributes to an understanding of the text in which it appears. (RI.4.7)	Sam Layla Maria Brittany
CC.4.Rinf.8	Explain how an author uses reasons and evidence to support particular points in a text. (RI.4.8)	
CC.4.Rinf.9	Integrate information from two texts on the same topic in order to write or speak about the subject knowledgeably. (RI.4.9)	
CC.4.Rinf.10	By the end of year, read and comprehend informational texts, including history/social studies, science, and technical texts, in the grades 4-5 text complexity band proficiently, with scaffolding as needed at the high end of the range. (RI.4.10)	

© National Geographic Learning, a part of Cengage Learning, Inc.
Grade 4 Assessment   **113**   Benchmark Test

The instructional materials in **National Geographic *Reach for Reading***, including the Practice Masters and Reteaching Masters, are invaluable resources you can use with your students when additional instruction or practice is needed.

Benchmark Reading Test

Description

The Form A Benchmark Reading Test contains 51 items. Students will respond to both multiple-choice and constructed-response items to assess Reading and Vocabulary skills.

Administering the Test

The approximate testing time for this test is 90 minutes. However, the Benchmark Assessments are not timed, so you have the flexibility to lengthen or shorten the testing times. If you wish to split testing into two sessions, end the first session at the end of Page 11.

Online Administration:

- Follow the directions in eAssessment.

Print Administration:

- Make one copy of the test for each student.
- Distribute one copy of the test to each student. Have the students write their name and the date on the test.
- Make sure that students have additional paper to respond to test questions that require a student-written response.

Both Administrations:

- Explain that the Benchmark Test will help the students know more about which Common Core State Standards they already know and which ones they need to work on.
- Remind students that some of the standards have not been taught yet. They should not worry if they do not know all the answers.
- If students have questions about the directions, you may read or paraphrase as necessary to make sure the students understand what to do.
- Tell the students the approximate amount of time they will have to complete their test.

Reading

Directions: Read the story. Then answer the questions about the story.

A Spider's Life

1   I'm not sure how other spiders feel about the life of a spider. Speaking for myself, I love it. I like to wake up early in the morning and just stare at the dancing threads of my web. The dewdrops sparkle in the sun like jewels. The droplets hang as if they're stopped in time, as if they just don't want to fall. I have to step carefully with my eight legs, so I don't knock the drops loose.

2   "You'd better get to work," I hear my neighbor Sammy call out from the web next door. Sammy is a good guy, but he thinks all that matters is work, work, work—and weaving webs as fast as you can. I've given him the nickname "Speedy Spider." He weaves so fast his eight legs just seem like a blur.

3   "OK, Speedy," I yell back. "But let me enjoy this splendid beauty for a moment." I can sense Speedy shaking his head at me. He's probably saying that I am lazy under his breath. I just know how he is.

4   I think of myself as an artist. I can imagine a design and then plan how to spin the threads and connect them to make the web as strong as possible. I'm like an architect, someone who designs what a building will look like. I guess you could call me a web architect. Speedy may be fast, but his webs fall apart easily. Mine seem to last forever. There was even a photograph of one of my webs in a magazine. I felt very proud.

5   I'm working on a new part of my web today. It's one of my best designs yet. This new part is going to be a creative area, where I can go to write poems and songs.

Reading

6   Hours later, just as darkness is falling, I hear a scream from next door. It's Speedy. He's frantic. He is hanging from a single thread, swinging like a circus performer. He's dangerously close to the ground.

7   "Some mean kid put a stick in my web and tore it all apart. I am trying not to panic, but my web is ruined! What will I do? I have nowhere to sleep tonight." Speedy is choking on his words, trying not to cry.

8   "Come on over," I say, inviting Speedy for the evening. "I have an extra web where you can stay. We'll have a delicious dinner of crunchy bugs, and I can help you weave a stronger web tomorrow."

9   I can sense Speedy sniffing back a tear of gratitude. I just know how he is.

---

1 Which of these describes the narrator's web at the beginning of the story?

Ⓐ full of beautiful dewdrops

Ⓑ built too fast and falling apart

Ⓒ home to several sleeping spiders

Ⓓ broken in places, with threads hanging down

2 What happens to Speedy's web?

Ⓐ Speedy builds a new part to make it larger.

Ⓑ A photograph of it appears in a magazine.

Ⓒ Speedy swings on it and it breaks.

Ⓓ A child tears it apart with a stick.

3 Which of these sentences describes the narrator of the story?

Ⓐ I think of myself as an artist.

Ⓑ I hear a scream from next door.

Ⓒ I have nowhere to sleep tonight.

Ⓓ I'm not sure how other spiders feel.

GO ON

Reading

4 Which of these is the theme of the story?

  Ⓐ Everything is better if you do it very fast.

  Ⓑ Staring at dewdrops all day will get you nowhere.

  Ⓒ Helping someone in need is more important than work.

  Ⓓ The most important thing in life is to work very hard.

5 Which of these best describes Speedy?

  Ⓐ He likes to stare at the threads of his web.

  Ⓑ He thinks all that matters is work, work, work.

  Ⓒ He likes to do tricks on his web, like swinging from thread to thread.

  Ⓓ He wants to be famous for building the most beautiful webs in the garden.

6 In paragraph 1, the phrase "the droplets hang as if they're stopped in time" means that the droplets —

  Ⓐ look like it has just started to rain.

  Ⓑ have been on the web many days.

  Ⓒ look like nothing can make them fall.

  Ⓓ appear old, as if the water is not fresh.

7 In paragraph 4, the word <u>architect</u> means a person who —

  Ⓐ takes photographs.

  Ⓑ designs buildings.

  Ⓒ builds buildings.

  Ⓓ paints pictures.

8 Read this sentence from paragraph 7.

> I am trying not to panic, but my web is ruined!

What does the word <u>panic</u> mean in this sentence?

  Ⓐ to feel sick

  Ⓑ to be afraid

  Ⓒ to want to fight

  Ⓓ to feel ashamed

GO ON

Reading

Directions: Read the story. Then answer the questions about the story.

Arachne, the Weaver

1   Arachne was a bold and proud young woman who lived long ago in a village of ancient Greece. She was full of pride because she had a gift for weaving.

2   Every day, she would stand at her loom weaving together colorful threads of wool. The tapestry she wove was a large cloth. It showed a picture that told a story. People watched her with amazement. She saw a design in her mind, and her fingers knew exactly how to turn her dream into a tapestry. The villagers whispered, "She is so good at her art, she must have been taught by the goddess of weaving, Athena."

3   When Arachne heard the villagers talking, she laughed. "How could Athena teach me anything when I am better at weaving than she is? I am the best weaver in the land."

4   The villagers gasped at her bragging. They warned her to be careful what she said or she would anger Athena. Arachne just laughed and went on weaving.

5   The goddess Athena heard everything and decided to teach Arachne a lesson. Athena came to visit Arachne, disguised as an old woman in ragged clothes. She warned Arachne never to compare herself to a god or goddess. This would anger the gods and they would punish her. Arachne

GO ON

Reading

said she would welcome a weaving contest with Athena. She knew she would win because she was the best weaver in the land. If she lost, she would accept any punishment.

6   Hearing Arachne's words, Athena threw off her disguise. "You are a boastful young woman!" she screamed. "You should not compare yourself with the gods and goddesses. We will *see* who the best weaver in the land is!"

7   The next day, right there, Arachne and Athena stood at their looms— the human and the goddess side by side. The villagers crowded around. A contest like this was something they had never seen before. No one made a sound. The two women worked from dawn until darkness.

8   Athena's work was beautiful. Her tapestry showed Athena with an olive tree and the sea god, Poseidon, in the ocean. Arachne's work, too, was amazingly beautiful; but the story she told in her tapestry made fun of the gods, especially Athena's father, Zeus.

9   Athena was furious. She tore up Arachne's tapestry and broke her loom into a hundred pieces. She reached out angrily and touched Arachne's forehead, making Arachne feel guilty and ashamed of her actions.

10   The villagers turned away and left Arachne alone and friendless. She fell to the ground sobbing. With one more touch of her hand, Athena then turned Arachne into a spider. "You have a gift for weaving, Arachne. Now, you will weave webs for the rest of your days."

GO ON

Reading

9 Which of these sentences from the story best describes Arachne's character?

- (A) The villagers crowded around.
- (B) Arachne and Athena stood at their looms.
- (C) Arachne was a bold and proud young woman.
- (D) We will see who the best weaver in the land is!

10 Where does the weaving contest take place?

- (A) in Athena's palace
- (B) in Arachne's village
- (C) in the olive garden of Athena
- (D) in the ocean kingdom of Poseidon

11 In paragraph 6, the words "Athena threw off her disguise" mean that Athena —

- (A) became a human.
- (B) was upset and made fun of Arachne.
- (C) took off her ragged clothes and showed her true self.
- (D) began to throw things at Arachne because she was angry.

12 Which of these sentences helps you know that Athena is angry with Arachne?

- (A) She tore up Arachne's tapestry.
- (B) She fell to the ground sobbing.
- (C) Athena came to visit Arachne.
- (D) No one made a sound.

13 What happens at the end of the story?

- (A) Arachne wins the weaving contest.
- (B) Athena turns Arachne into a spider.
- (C) Athena destroys the village because she is so angry.
- (D) Arachne learns to appreciate Athena's talent as a weaver.

14 What words best describe Athena?

- (A) powerful and proud
- (B) smart and friendly
- (C) kind and helpful
- (D) lazy and messy

GO ON

Reading

15 Which of these best summarizes the story?

Ⓐ A beautiful cloth is worth its weight in gold.

Ⓑ A village is amazed by an excellent weaver.

Ⓒ A young woman uses her talent to help others.

Ⓓ A young woman brags too much and is punished.

16 The word proud is used in paragraph 1. What is the **opposite** of proud?

Ⓐ beautiful

Ⓑ humble

Ⓒ crazy

Ⓓ angry

---

17 How are the themes in "A Spider's Life" and "Arachne, the Weaver" alike? How are they different? Think about how the characters act toward others who have the same skills they do.

GO ON

Reading

Directions: Read the story. Then answer the questions about the story.

The Gift

1   Adisa and Oni had been friends since they were little. They were cousins, but more than that, they seemed to have the same thoughts at the same time. They liked to wear dresses with the same colorful patterns. Each made a delicate bead necklace and gave it to the other as a special friendship present. They wore the necklaces everywhere.

2   Because their village was known for its weaving, the girls studied weaving with the women of the village. Both became good weavers and worked hard to become the best artists they could be. They loved the feel of the stiff cloth and the interesting and bold designs they could create with the crisscrossing of thick threads.

3   One day, the head of the regional school came to the village and told all the girls that she could choose just one girl to come to the school. She would choose the best weaver in the village.

4   Adisa and Oni looked at each other. Surely one of them would be chosen. But which one? And what would happen to the other? Each knew how important education was. Each really wanted to go to the school. But only one could go.

5   Adisa and Oni began to work even harder on their weaving to win the spot at the school. Each one thought, "I'm better than she is. They should pick me for the school." They began to drift apart and even stopped talking to each other.

GO ON

Reading

6   When their grandmother fell ill, they still worked hard at their weaving, but they went to visit her every day. They went at different times so they wouldn't bump into each other. Grandmother got sicker and weaker. She didn't have the strength to move. When Adisa or Oni visited, she could not even talk. She had lost the sparkle in her eyes and didn't even seem to see them.

7   "We have to do something," Adisa said to Oni one day, breaking their long silence. "Yes, we have to help Grandmother right away," Oni agreed.

8   They decided to weave her a wonderful, colorful cloth—together! They worked side by side at the loom and forgot about their fight for the one place at the school. When they were finished, they tiptoed into Grandmother's bedroom holding the woven cloth behind them.

9   "We made this together," they said at the same time and brought the weaving out from its hiding place.

10   "It is lovely," Grandmother said weakly. "I can see each of you woven into the threads. But what makes me especially happy is to see two girls who are such good friends." And for the first time in many weeks, Grandmother lifted her head and smiled.

---

18 How do Adisa and Oni feel about each other at the beginning of the story?

Ⓐ They fight over little things.

Ⓑ They are almost like sisters.

Ⓒ Each thinks the other is a better weaver.

Ⓓ Each wants to beat the other to win the spot at school.

19 What does had lost the sparkle in her eyes mean in paragraph 6?

Ⓐ was forgetful

Ⓑ could not see

Ⓒ was unfriendly

Ⓓ was weak and tired

GO ON

Name _____   Date _____

20 Which of these sentences marks a point where the story changes direction?

    Ⓐ Grandmother got sicker and weaker.

    Ⓑ She would choose the best weaver in the village.

    Ⓒ Adisa and Oni had been friends since they were little.

    Ⓓ They liked to wear dresses with the same colorful patterns.

21 Which sentence best summarizes the story?

    Ⓐ Two girls work hard in school because their grandmother wants them to succeed.

    Ⓑ Two girls who have been friends for a long time have a fight and stop speaking to each other.

    Ⓒ Two girls work hard at becoming good weavers because the village is known for its weaving.

    Ⓓ Two girls who want to get into a school forget their friendship until their grandmother becomes sick and they make a gift for her.

22 What does "they tiptoed into Grandmother's bedroom" mean in paragraph 8?

    Ⓐ They peeked in to see how she was.

    Ⓑ They put on dance shoes before they went in.

    Ⓒ They went in quietly, lifting their heels to avoid making noise.

    Ⓓ They wore special socks for Grandmother to make her happy.

23 The words "I can see each of you woven into the threads" in paragraph 10 mean that —

    Ⓐ the girls put their pictures in the weaving.

    Ⓑ the girls included some special objects in the cloth.

    Ⓒ Grandmother can see their personalities in the weaving.

    Ⓓ Grandmother enjoyed watching them at the loom as they wove her gift.

24 Think about themes in the stories "Arachne, the Weaver" and "The Gift." Compare the problems that are caused by the characters' faults. Compare the ways the characters change in each story.

GO ON

Reading

Directions: Read the article. Then answer the questions about the article.

The Transcontinental Railroad

1   In the mid-1800s, travel from one part of the United States to another was slow and difficult. Journeys from coast to coast were often dangerous and took many weeks. People traveled in ships, covered wagons, or stagecoaches.

2   Then, Americans decided to build a railroad across the United States. They hoped it would make the country strong. After several years, people finally agreed that the railroad should follow a route through the central part of the country. In 1862, President Abraham Lincoln signed a law for the railroad to be built. It would be called the Transcontinental Railroad because it would go from one end of our continent to the other.

3   Two railroad companies were chosen to build the railroad. The Central Pacific Railroad started in Sacramento, California, building tracks eastward. Later they connected them west to Oakland. The Union Pacific Railroad started in Omaha, Nebraska, building tracks westward. Omaha was across the Missouri River from tracks that already went to the East Coast.

4   Thousands of people helped build the railroad. Many workers were immigrants who had moved to the United States from China and Europe. The work was very hard. They had no machines to level the ground, lay the rails, or drive the spikes to hold down the rails. The workers tunneled through mountains and built bridges. They worked in the hot desert sun and the freezing mountain winters.

GO ON

Reading

5   Finally, the tracks met in the Utah Territory in 1869. Central Pacific drove an engine from the west, and Union Pacific drove one from the east. The two engines stopped, facing each other a few feet apart. The last bit of track was put down and nailed into place with spikes of gold and silver. (They were later replaced with iron spikes.) The country was connected at last.

6   The Transcontinental Railroad brought many changes to our country. Sadly, many Native Americans were pushed from their lands. Many of the bison the Native Americans had been using for food, clothing, and shelter disappeared. But the Transcontinental Railroad brought good changes, too. People, freight, mail, and ideas could travel quickly and easily. A person could travel from the East Coast to the West Coast in eight days! The Civil War was over, and the Transcontinental Railroad helped bring the country together and make it strong.

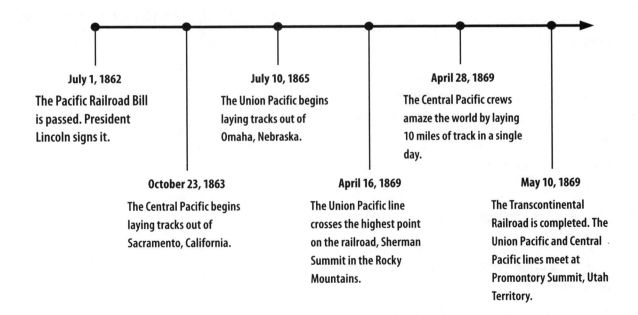

July 1, 1862
The Pacific Railroad Bill is passed. President Lincoln signs it.

October 23, 1863
The Central Pacific begins laying tracks out of Sacramento, California.

July 10, 1865
The Union Pacific begins laying tracks out of Omaha, Nebraska.

April 16, 1869
The Union Pacific line crosses the highest point on the railroad, Sherman Summit in the Rocky Mountains.

April 28, 1869
The Central Pacific crews amaze the world by laying 10 miles of track in a single day.

May 10, 1869
The Transcontinental Railroad is completed. The Union Pacific and Central Pacific lines meet at Promontory Summit, Utah Territory.

GO ON

Reading

25 What is the main idea of this passage?

   Ⓐ The Transcontinental Railroad was built during the Civil War.

   Ⓑ Thousands of people worked to build the Transcontinental Railroad.

   Ⓒ Building the Transcontinental Railroad was difficult, but it was worth it.

   Ⓓ Two companies worked together to build the Transcontinental Railroad.

26 Why was the Transcontinental Railroad built?

   Ⓐ to help end the Civil War

   Ⓑ to give jobs to thousands of people

   Ⓒ to connect and strengthen the country

   Ⓓ to show that two companies could cooperate

27 What does the author say about how the route for the Transcontinental Railroad was chosen?

   Ⓐ President Lincoln decided which route to use.

   Ⓑ The southern route was the most popular choice.

   Ⓒ The companies were allowed to choose the route.

   Ⓓ People disagreed at first about the route that should be used.

28 Which detail supports the idea that the railroad changed the United States?

   Ⓐ President Abraham Lincoln signed a law.

   Ⓑ People, freight, and ideas could travel fast and easily.

   Ⓒ Immigrants worked in the hot sun and freezing winters.

   Ⓓ The last bit of track was nailed down with gold and silver spikes.

29 What kind of structure is used to organize the information in the last paragraph?

   Ⓐ A cause and its effects are explained.

   Ⓑ Details are compared and contrasted.

   Ⓒ A problem and its solution are described.

   Ⓓ Events are listed in the order in which they happened.

GO ON

Reading

30 Read this sentence from paragraph 2.

> It would be called the Transcontinental Railroad because it would go from one end of our continent to the other.

The word <u>transcontinental</u> refers to something that passes —

Ⓐ into a continent.

Ⓑ above continents.

Ⓒ across a continent.

Ⓓ between continents.

31 Read this sentence from paragraph 4.

> Many workers were immigrants who had moved to the United States from China and Europe.

The word <u>immigrants</u> means people who —

Ⓐ have families.

Ⓑ work on railroads.

Ⓒ are looking for jobs.

Ⓓ come to a new country.

---

32 In what ways does the timeline help you understand the Transcontinental Railroad? What information does it give that is not in the article? Give examples in your answer.

GO ON

Reading

Directions: Read the article. Then answer the questions about the article.

Underground Surprise

1   Quaking aspens, or trembling aspens, are slender trees with white or gray bark. Their round leaves tremble and dance in the smallest breeze. Aspens grow all over the United States. In autumn, their leaves turn a beautiful, bright yellow or gold. Most people love aspens but are not amazed by them.

2   Scientists, however, think aspens are amazing! Here are some reasons why. Aspen trees grow in groves (called "clones"). A grove of aspens looks like a forest with many separate trees. But in fact, each aspen tree in a grove is linked to all the others. They are all part of the same plant!

3   The first aspen tree that starts a grove sprouts from a seed. As it grows, its roots spread out in every direction. Then little shoots begin to grow up from the roots. They grow into aspen trees and are called *ramets*. They stay connected to the root system of the first tree and also add their own roots to the system. As older trees die, more and more new ones appear. They are all part of one huge plant.

4   The biggest aspen grove ever found is in Utah. It has over 40,000 ramets, or trees. It is very big and heavy. It is called the most massive living thing on Earth. It weighs over 13 million pounds! It covers more than one hundred acres. Remember, it is all one plant. Scientists have named the grove "Pando," which means in Latin "I spread." Scientists can't tell exactly how old Pando is, but they think the grove is many thousands of years old.

Reading

5   Here are some reasons an aspen grove can grow as large as Pando. The trees share food and water with one another through the root system. Some ramets may be growing in wet dirt, while others are growing on the other side of the grove where the soil is dry. The ramets in the wet dirt will send others water through the roots. Ramets growing in dirt that has good nutrients help feed other ramets in the grove by sending them nutrients. If a fire burns some trees in a grove, many new ones quickly sprout from the roots. The aspens in an aspen grove are beautiful trees. But the most amazing part of the grove is hidden underground!

---

33 Which of these details best supports the idea that aspen groves can grow to be very large because all the trees are connected?

  Ⓐ Aspens grow in many parts of the country.

  Ⓑ The biggest aspen grove ever found is in Utah.

  Ⓒ Each ramet is a copy of the very first tree in the grove.

  Ⓓ Ramets growing in wet dirt send water to other trees in the grove.

34 How has Pando stayed alive for thousands of years?

  Ⓐ Pando's trunks are healthy.

  Ⓑ Fires rarely burn aspen groves like Pando.

  Ⓒ New ramets keep sprouting from Pando's roots.

  Ⓓ People protect Pando because it is so large and so old.

35 Aspen trees in a grove are all part of the same plant because they sprout —

  Ⓐ from seeds.

  Ⓑ in the same place.

  Ⓒ from the same roots.

  Ⓓ after a fire burns older trees.

36 The author gives reasons why scientists are amazed by aspens. The author most likely gives those reasons in order to —

  Ⓐ prove that scientists are curious.

  Ⓑ interest people in studying science.

  Ⓒ help more people realize that aspens really are unique.

  Ⓓ show that aspens are quite hard for people to understand.

GO ON

Reading

37 Which of these is the best summary of this article?

Ⓐ Aspen trees sprout up from roots. This lets them get very large.

Ⓑ Aspen trees can grow in groves. One grove of aspens is the biggest living thing on Earth.

Ⓒ Aspen trees have leaves that dance. The leaves turn yellow in autumn. Aspens can send other aspens food and water.

Ⓓ Aspen trees grow in groves. All the trees in a grove are part of one plant connected by roots. Aspen groves can get very large.

38 How is the information in the third paragraph organized?

Ⓐ Questions are asked and answered.

Ⓑ Details are compared and contrasted.

Ⓒ A problem is described along with its solution.

Ⓓ Events are described in the order in which they happen.

39 In paragraph 4, what does the word massive mean?

Ⓐ heavy and large

Ⓑ famous and popular

Ⓒ proud and important

Ⓓ beautiful and colorful

40 In paragraph 5, the word nutrients means about the same as —

Ⓐ heat.

Ⓑ food.

Ⓒ rocks.

Ⓓ leaves.

GO ON

Reading

41 Which word from the article best fits in this sentence?

> Aspen trees can grow in many different kinds of
> _____, even when they are part of the same grove.

Ⓐ soil

Ⓑ ramet

Ⓒ clones

Ⓓ shoots

42 Read this dictionary entry.

> **root** (rüt) *noun* **1** the part of a plant that grows underground **2** the base of
> a tooth or piece of hair **3** the source of a thing **4** the basic part of a word
> to which affixes are added

Which meaning of <u>root</u> is used in this sentence from paragraph 3?

> As it grows, its <u>roots</u> spread out in every direction.

Ⓐ meaning 1

Ⓑ meaning 2

Ⓒ meaning 3

Ⓓ meaning 4

GO ON

Reading

Directions: Read the passage. Then answer the questions about the passage.

Visiting an Aspen Grove

1   I walked into the grove of quaking aspens with my aunt and turned in a slow circle on the path. All around me were the white trunks of aspen trees growing upward toward the sun. I realized why they are called quaking aspens. It's because their small, round leaves never stop quaking, or trembling. I could hear the leaves rustle, making a "Shhhhh" sound. I also heard a symphony of happy bird songs. It really was kind of pretty.

2   My aunt Maya agreed, but she told me it was more than just pretty. She explained that an aspen grove was an amazing place. I pointed at a tree. It has a trunk, branches, and leaves. I told her that I thought it ranked pretty low on the amazing scale.

3   Aunt Maya snorted. She explained that aspens were not *just* trees. She had learned about them when she studied plants in a botany class in college. She told me that all the trees around us were part of one giant aspen plant, called a "grove" or a "clone." I couldn't believe that all these trees weren't separate plants.

4   Then Aunt Maya said something surprising. She said that the aspens were all growing from one huge underground root system. Of course, to prove that, she said she would have to take some samples to a laboratory. She could scrape some tiny bits from several trees and put them in containers. Then she could look at them with a microscope and do some other tests. She would see that they all contain cells from the grove's first tree. She explained that each tree was like a twin of the other trees.

GO ON

5   We continued hiking down the trail. The trees sure didn't look like they were all part of the same plant. My aunt told me to look more closely. She said that all the trees in the grove had branches that came out of their trunk at the same angle. If we went to another grove, all of their branches would be alike, but coming out of their trunks at a different angle from the trees in this grove. Then she told me another neat thing. All the trees in the grove we were in would get their leaves at exactly the same time in the spring! When aspens are leafing out, it is easy to tell which trees belong to the same grove. Trees from another grove, even if it's very near, will get their leaves at a different time.

6   It still was strange to think that we were walking through one giant living thing that was under our feet and growing all around us. She grinned and said it was strange, but it was also very cool. She said that was what brought her out to the aspen groves, and she was glad she could share it with me.

---

43 Which detail best supports Aunt Maya's idea that aspen groves are amazing places?

  Ⓐ All the aspen trees have white bark.

  Ⓑ All the aspen trees are part of the same plant.

  Ⓒ All the aspen trees are different ages and sizes.

  Ⓓ All the aspen trees have leaves that turn colors in the fall.

44 In the passage, Aunt Maya tells the author that she learned about aspens in a botany class in college. The author most likely gives that information to show the reader that —

  Ⓐ Aunt Maya's information about aspens is true.

  Ⓑ many people think aspens are strange.

  Ⓒ Aunt Maya is older than her nephew.

  Ⓓ the hike she is leading will be safe.

GO ON ➡

Reading

45 Read this sentence from paragraph 1.

> I also heard a symphony of
> happy bird songs.

The Greek root *phon-* means <u>sound</u>, so the
word <u>symphony</u> probably means a kind of —

(A) party.

(B) game.

(C) music.

(D) dance.

46 According to the passage, a clue that a
grove of aspens is part of one plant is
that they —

(A) grow near each other.

(B) have small, round leaves.

(C) are found next to hiking trails.

(D) sprout leaves at the same time.

47 According to the passage, what is one way to
prove that an aspen tree is part of a grove?

(A) look at how old the trees are

(B) listen to the birds that live there

(C) study the way their leaves tremble

(D) look at samples with a microscope

48 Read this sentence from paragraph 4.

> She said that the aspens were
> all growing from one huge
> underground root system.

The phrase <u>root system</u> means the
roots are —

(A) protected.

(B) connected.

(C) growing quickly.

(D) important to the plant.

49 Which of these sentences is the best summary
of this passage?

(A) An aunt teaches her nephew about aspen
groves during a hike.

(B) An aunt and her nephew talk about ways
to study botany.

(C) An aunt takes her nephew on a hike in an
aspen grove.

(D) An aunt shares information about many
unusual plants.

GO ON

Reading

50 Read this dictionary entry.

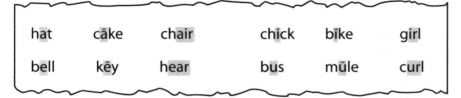

bo•ta•ny ('bä•tə•nē) *noun* **1** the scientific study of plants

Pronunciation Key:

hat	cāke	chair	chick	bīke	girl
bell	kēy	hear	bus	mūle	curl

Using the information in this entry, the second vowel sound in <u>botany</u> sounds most like the vowel in —

Ⓐ hat.

Ⓑ bus.

Ⓒ curl.

Ⓓ chair.

51 Describe the focus and information in "Underground Surprise" and "Visiting an Aspen Grove. " Show ways in which the focus and information in each text are different. Use examples from both passages to support your answer.

Benchmark Writing Test

Description

The Form A Benchmark Writing Test contains 16 items. Students will respond to both multiple-choice and constructed-response items to assess Writing and Language skills.

Administering the Test

The approximate testing time for this test is 90 minutes. However, the Benchmark Assessments are not timed, so you have the flexibility to lengthen or shorten the testing times. If you wish to split testing into two sessions, end the first session after students complete item 13 (the first draft for the research prompt).

Online Administration:

- Follow the directions in eAssessment.

Print Administration:

- Make one copy of the test for each student.

- Distribute one copy of the test to each student. Have the students write their name and the date on the test.

- Make sure that students have additional paper to prepare for and write first and final drafts for the test questions that require a student-written response.

Both Administrations:

- Explain that the Benchmark Test will help the students know more about which Common Core State Standards they already know and which ones they need to work on.

- Remind students that some of the standards have not been taught yet. They should not worry if they do not know all the answers.

- If students have questions about the directions, you may read or paraphrase as necessary to make sure the students understand what to do. If students have difficulty reading the items or provided sources, you may read as necessary.

- Tell the students the approximate amount of time they will have to complete their test.

- Students may not use their books during the test. They may use a dictionary when responding to writing prompts, but it may not be used for the multiple-choice items.

NOTE: Writing Standard 6 in the Common Core State Standards assesses students' use of computer technology to produce or publish writing. If you wish to assess this standard, have students take the test in eAssessment. Alternatively, if you are using the print version, you may have students use a word processor to respond to the writing prompts.

Writing

Directions: Read the paragraph. Then answer the questions.

---

(1) I want to tell you about a wonderful book _____ I read last week. (2) I _____ for a good adventure story, and I found it. (3) A good adventure story _____ me interested right from the start. (4) Otherwise, I get bored and start looking _____. (5) The book I found is called *Treasure of the Tortugas*. (6) The librarian recommended it to me. (7) She said, this book is about a boy who sneaks onto a pirate ship. (8) That sounded exciting, so I checked it out and started reading. (9) I am so glad! (10) _____ is so much action right from the start! (11) The pirates have sword fights, and the boy swings from ropes to try to get away. (12) I loved this book. (13) I hope they make it into a movie someday.

---

1 Which answer correctly completes sentence 1?

Ⓐ who

Ⓑ that

Ⓒ when

Ⓓ which

2 Which answer correctly completes sentence 2?

Ⓐ is looking

Ⓑ be looking

Ⓒ was looking

Ⓓ were looking

GO ON

Writing

3 Which answer correctly completes sentence 3?

Ⓐ do get

Ⓑ can gets

Ⓒ may gets

Ⓓ must get

4 Which answer correctly completes sentence 4?

Ⓐ of interesting reading

Ⓑ at read something else

Ⓒ into more exciting to read

Ⓓ for something else to read

5 What is the correct way to write sentence 7?

Ⓐ She said, "This book is about a boy who sneaks onto a pirate ship."

Ⓑ She said, that book is about a boy who sneaks onto a pirate ship.

Ⓒ "She said, this book is about a boy who sneaks onto a pirate ship".

Ⓓ Correct as is

6 Which answer correctly completes sentence 10?

Ⓐ Their

Ⓑ There

Ⓒ They're

Ⓓ They are

GO ON

Writing

Directions: Read the paragraph. Then answer the questions.

> **(1)** Maria, _____ is new at school, needed my help yesterday. **(2)** Her family just arrived in the United States and she doesn't speak English very well. **(3)** Since I speak Spanish, I _____ her every day from now on. **(4)** She is a really nice girl. **(5)** She lives in the red large building near my house. **(6)** Maria's family comes from Nicaragua, which is a country in _____. **(7)** Maria is really good at math and doesn't need my help at all with that! **(8)** She just needs me to translate what the teacher says sometimes. **(9)** Because Maria is so smart. **(10)** Will learn English quickly. **(11)** Right now, I am glad I am there to help. **(12)** Maybe she could help me with my math!

7 Which answer correctly completes sentence 1?

Ⓐ who

Ⓑ that

Ⓒ which

Ⓓ whose

8 What is the correct way to write sentence 2?

Ⓐ Her family just arrived in the United States and she don't speak English very well.

Ⓑ Her family just arrived in the United States, and she doesn't speak English very well.

Ⓒ Her family's just arrived in the United States and she doesn't speak English very well.

Ⓓ Correct as is

GO ON

Writing

9 Which answer correctly completes sentence 3?

Ⓐ be helping

Ⓑ will be help

Ⓒ will helping

Ⓓ will be helping

10 What is the correct way to write sentence 5?

Ⓐ She lives in the large red building near my house.

Ⓑ She lives in the red large building near mine house.

Ⓒ She live in the red large building near my house.

Ⓓ Correct as is

11 Which answer correctly completes sentence 6?

Ⓐ central America

Ⓑ central america

Ⓒ Central america

Ⓓ Central America

12 What is the correct way to write sentences 9 and 10?

Ⓐ Because Maria is so smart. She will learn English quickly.

Ⓑ Because Maria is so smart she will learn English quickly.

Ⓒ Because Maria is so smart, she will learn English quickly.

Ⓓ Correct as is

GO ON

Writing

13 Your class is writing reports for Animal Week. Your report will be about how farmed ostriches and wild ostriches are alike and different. First, read Source 1 and Source 2. Then take notes and plan your writing. You may use a graphic organizer like the one on the next page to organize your thoughts. Then, on a separate sheet of paper, write your rough draft.

Source 1

from *Ostrich Farming Weekly* magazine, February 2012

Quick History of Ostrich Farming

by Wanda Fuller

Ostrich farming started in South Africa in the 1800s. At that time, people were interested mostly in the feathers. Ostrich feathers were used to decorate hats and clothing.

Today, ostriches are farmed all over the world. Feathers are only a small part of the business now. The meat and the hide (or skin) of the ostriches are more important. The meat is a lot like beef but has less fat. The hide is very valuable. It is used for making expensive shoes and purses.

A farmer needs less land to raise ostriches than to raise cows. Ostriches also grow up very quickly. Ostrich chicks grow 1 foot per month for the first 6 or 7 months. A full-grown ostrich produces 70 pounds of meat, 14 square feet of hide, and 2 pounds of feathers.

GO ON

Writing

Source 2

www.WildWorld.org/ostrich

Ostriches in the Wild

Quick Facts

- Ostriches live in the dry plains and desert areas of Africa.

- They are the biggest birds in the world, but they cannot fly.

- A full-grown male can be 9 feet tall and weigh 350 pounds.

- Ostriches can run at speeds of up to 45 miles per hour.

- Ostriches live in small groups of about 12 birds.

- The females in a group lay eggs in a common nest. The main male and female take turns sitting on the eggs.

- An ostrich egg can measure 6 inches across and weigh 3 pounds.

Graphic Organizer

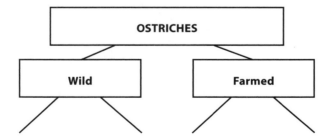

Writing

14 Write the final version of your report about ostriches on a separate sheet of paper. Before you write, you may

- read the sources, your notes, and the graphic organizer

- review and revise your rough draft.

15 Write a narrative about an outdoor activity with family or friends. Do your writing on a separate sheet of paper. Be sure to

- tell what you did to get ready for the activity and what happened during the activity

- use time-order words to tell clearly when things happened

- give enough specific details so readers can understand what it was like to take part in the activity.

16 Imagine that your principal is trying to decide whether students at your school should wear school uniforms. Write a letter to your principal telling your opinion about school uniforms. Give facts and reasons to support your opinion. Do your writing on a separate sheet of paper.

Score	
_____/12 multiple-choice	
_____/4 research and draft	
_____/24 expository prompt	
_____/24 narrative prompt	
_____/24 opinion prompt	

Benchmark Reading Test, Form B, Copy Masters 34–54

Benchmark Reading Test

Description

The Form B Benchmark Reading Test contains 51 items. Students will respond to both multiple-choice and constructed-response items to assess Reading and Vocabulary skills.

Administering the Test

The approximate testing time for this test is 90 minutes. However, the Benchmark Assessments are not timed, so you have the flexibility to lengthen or shorten the testing times. If you wish to split testing into two sessions, end the first session at the end of Page 43.

Online Administration:

- Follow the directions in eAssessment.

Print Administration:

- Make one copy of the test for each student.

- Distribute one copy of the test to each student. Have the students write their name and the date on the test.

- Make sure that students have additional paper to respond to test questions that require a student-written response.

Both Administrations:

- Explain that the Benchmark Test will help the students know more about which Common Core State Standards they already know and which ones they need to work on.

- Remind students that some of the standards have not been taught yet. They should not worry if they do not know all the answers.

- If students have questions about the directions, you may read or paraphrase as necessary to make sure the students understand what to do.

- Tell the students the approximate amount of time they will have to complete their test.

Reading

Form B

Directions: Read the story. Then answer the questions about the story.

The Perfect Dive

1   Today is our final swim meet of the summer. I don't mean to brag, but so far I've won all six diving competitions this season. Everyone is talking about how I might go to the Junior Olympics. Mainly, though, I'm just a girl who loves to swim and dive. Winning is just an extra gift.

2   I have loved the water since I was six years old, and have been competing in swim meets since I was eight. My mom says she's surprised I don't have fins like a fish.

3   I'm a good diver, but I have one problem. I hate doing a back dive. In competition, I have to do one front dive and one back dive. These are required dives; that means I must do them. I also have to do two optional dives, or dives that I choose myself.

4   Why do I hate the back dive? You have to balance on the end of the board with your back to the water, standing very still and trying not to wobble back and forth. When you lift off, you have to imagine where the water is because you can't see it until the very end. I feel lost.

5   My coach has taught me to focus my thoughts so that I don't hear or see anything around me when I'm diving. It's a good skill because people talk and babies cry and cell phones ring. My coach also asks me to take a moment to imagine the dive before I do it. If my mind can see it, my body can do it, he says. It is hard to do, but I've been practicing.

GO ON

Reading

6   There are hundreds of people here watching today. I'm ready. The first dive is my front dive. I imagine myself as a graceful bird. I'm up, flying, and into the water without a splash. When I come up for air, the crowd is cheering and my family and friends are smiling. The judges give me a high score.

7   I do my two optional dives next, and they are both given high scores. I have only my back dive to do well, and I will go to the Junior Olympics.

8   I walk carefully to the end of the board, turn, and balance. I block out all the noise from the crowd and begin to imagine myself doing a perfect back dive. In my mind, I go up, arch my back, drop my head, and enter the water without a splash. I take my time. I tell my brain I can do this. I see myself doing this. And, with that, I push off the board—and do it.

9   When I burst to the surface, the crowd is cheering and I'm smiling because I'll be going to the Junior Olympics. Maybe I'm starting to like my back dive after all!

---

1 Which sentence helps the reader understand how the girl feels about swimming and diving?

Ⓐ The first dive is my front dive.

Ⓑ I also have to do two optional dives.

Ⓒ I have loved the water since I was six years old.

Ⓓ There are hundreds of people here watching today.

2 Which words from the story tell the reader that the main character has some confidence?

Ⓐ I'm a good diver.

Ⓑ Why do I hate the back dive?

Ⓒ Today is our final swim meet of the summer.

Ⓓ My mom says she's surprised I don't have fins.

GO ON

Reading

3 Which of these is the best summary of the first paragraph?

   Ⓐ A girl has won all the diving competitions this summer.

   Ⓑ A girl has been in six swim meets this summer and today is the last one.

   Ⓒ A girl who wants to win the Junior Olympics brags to everyone about her diving skills.

   Ⓓ A girl who loves swimming and diving, whether she wins or not, might go to the Junior Olympics.

4 What is the theme of the story?

   Ⓐ Everyone should try being a diver.

   Ⓑ Winning is the most important thing.

   Ⓒ No one should ever be afraid of anything.

   Ⓓ Working hard and focusing can help you do well.

5 Which of these sentences from the story best tells about the girl?

   Ⓐ Winning is just an extra gift.

   Ⓑ I walk carefully to the end of the board.

   Ⓒ When I burst to the surface, the crowd is cheering.

   Ⓓ These are required dives; that means I must do them.

6 What is the setting of the story?

   Ⓐ the Junior Olympics

   Ⓑ a large party for a girl's family and friends

   Ⓒ a sports camp for children

   Ⓓ the last swim meet before the Junior Olympics

7 What word has a similar meaning to the word required in paragraph 3?

   Ⓐ chosen

   Ⓑ difficult

   Ⓒ awkward

   Ⓓ necessary

8 What does the word balance mean in paragraph 4?

   Ⓐ keep from falling over

   Ⓑ dream about something

   Ⓒ think about many things

   Ⓓ jump from one place to another

9 What does "I imagine myself as a graceful bird" mean in paragraph 6?

   Ⓐ The girl uses her arms like wings.

   Ⓑ The girl wants her dive to be like an elegant flight.

   Ⓒ The girl has been studying in school the way birds fly.

   Ⓓ The girl wants to be able to look at the crowd from way up high.

GO ON

Reading

Directions: Read the story. Then answer the questions about the story.

Doing What Comes Naturally

1   "Ball four!" the umpire called loudly, with a thrust of his arm. Jerry looked sheepishly at Coach. This was the third batter Jerry had walked this inning. Things weren't going all that well. He was hoping Coach wouldn't take him out of the game, but the team could not afford any more walks.

2   Coach gave Jerry a look that said, "It's no use crying over spilled milk." Coach also held up five fingers, which meant, "Remember the five things I told you: relax, breathe, focus, pitch to the chosen spot, and follow through." Jerry took a deep breath as the next batter came up to the plate. He focused, wound up, and threw, with Herculean strength. The ball sizzled through the air like a rocket. Unfortunately, it was more like a misguided rocket. The ball went wild and hit the dirt way outside of home plate.

3   "Ball one," said the umpire, and Jerry sighed. He thought back to the day he had begged Coach to let him pitch. He had always dreamed of being a pitcher. Pitchers were the most important position in defense on the team. He had practiced for weeks in his backyard, throwing pitch after pitch into the hole in the tire that his dad had strung up on a tree. He was beginning the think it was no use. He just wasn't a good pitcher.

4   Coach was coming out to the mound. "Sorry, Jerry. I have to replace you now."

GO ON

Reading

5   "I understand, Coach," Jerry muttered and walked slowly back to the dugout with his head lowered.

6   The next day at practice, Coach took Jerry aside. "I'm moving you to right field."

7   "But Coach, that's a place for losers," Jerry protested. He was sorry as soon as he said it, but Coach pounced.

8   "Hey, wait a minute! Every position is important on this team. Do you want to play or not?"

9   "Yes, sir," Jerry said and ran to right field without another word.

10   It may have been luck or just a strange coincidence, but the very next ball that was hit came straight for right field. It was a long ball, full of power. Jerry turned and ran deeper into the field. At just the last moment, he reached over his shoulder and grabbed the fly ball in his glove. The team cheered. Very few players would have made that catch, and Jerry had done it. Back on the bench, Coach shook his head in wonder and said quietly, "He's a natural."

11   Jerry beamed and held up his glove proudly. He knew then and there that right field was his position. He had found his place.

GO ON

Reading

10 What is the best summary of this story?

   Ⓐ A boy works hard but cannot succeed in baseball.

   Ⓑ A boy tries something new and finds he is good at it.

   Ⓒ A father helps his son to become a pitcher on the baseball team.

   Ⓓ A coach has to make a difficult decision about a boy on his team.

11 What happens in the first paragraph of the story?

   Ⓐ Coach moves the pitcher to right field.

   Ⓑ Coach takes the pitcher out of the game.

   Ⓒ The pitcher walks three batters in one inning.

   Ⓓ The pitcher throws a ball that sizzles through the air.

12 What is the meaning of "It's no use crying over spilled milk" in paragraph 2?

   Ⓐ If you spill something, wipe it up before someone slips on it.

   Ⓑ Only children cry, so it's better to be grown-up about a bad situation.

   Ⓒ There's plenty of milk in the world, so spilled milk is not a big problem.

   Ⓓ People shouldn't worry about things that are done and can't be changed.

13 Which sentence tells us something about Jerry's dream of being a pitcher?

   Ⓐ He had practiced for weeks in his backyard.

   Ⓑ Every position is important on this team.

   Ⓒ Coach was coming out to the mound.

   Ⓓ The team cheered.

14 What does "Herculean strength" mean in paragraph 2?

   Ⓐ strength used to help others

   Ⓑ strength that does not last long

   Ⓒ strength that people make fun of

   Ⓓ strength greater than most people have

GO ON

Reading

15 Read this dictionary entry.

straight ('strāt) *adjective* **1** something without curves or bends **2** honest or fair **3** staying on course

Pronunciation Key:

| hat | cāke | chair | | chick | bīke | girl |
| bell | kēy | hear | | bus | mūle | curl |

Using the dictionary entry, the <u>a</u> in the word <u>straight</u> sounds most like the vowel in —

Ⓐ hat

Ⓑ key

Ⓒ bell

Ⓓ cake

16 What are the similarities and differences between "The Perfect Dive" and "Doing What Comes Naturally" in the way the stories are told? From which point of view is each story told?

GO ON ➡

Reading

Directions: Read the poem. Then answer the questions about the poem.

I Want to Fly

1   Some days I feel I want to fly
    With body light and pure as air,
    To reach way up and touch the sky
    And leave behind my daily cares.

2   I search for courage like a lion's
    And hunt for values to go far.
    With hero's heart brave as Orion's,
    My eyes shine brightly as a star.

3   Some days I feel I want to fly
    With wing-heeled shoes like Mercury,
    To move like lightning, passing by
    The things that I don't wish to see.

4   As I grow up I want to be
    A person doing what is right,
    Always steady, strong as a tree
    Giving others hope that's bright.

5   Some days I feel I want to fly
    To let myself be truly free,
    To see things with an honest eye—
    I only want to just be me.

GO ON

Reading

17 The poem's title "I Want to Fly" means that the speaker wants to —

Ⓐ learn how to fly an airplane.

Ⓑ be free to find out who he or she really is.

Ⓒ learn more about the sun, moon, stars, and sky.

Ⓓ be able to fly like people in myths and fairy tales.

18 Which of these lines from the poem is about something the writer does **not** like?

Ⓐ *To reach way up and touch the sky*

Ⓑ *And leave behind my daily cares*

Ⓒ *My eyes shine brightly as a star*

Ⓓ *A person doing what is right*

19 What is the theme of this poem?

Ⓐ how to learn to fly

Ⓑ why you should never tell a lie

Ⓒ growing up to become yourself

Ⓓ learning about the sky and stars

20 The line "I search for courage like a lion's" in stanza 2 means that the speaker —

Ⓐ wants to be brave as a lion.

Ⓑ thinks that people are afraid of lions.

Ⓒ wants to be able to learn more about lions.

Ⓓ wishes for a strong voice like the roar of a lion.

GO ON

Reading

21 The phrase "And hunt for values to go far" in stanza 2 means that the speaker wants —

Ⓐ quality objects at low prices.

Ⓑ an honest way to make money.

Ⓒ beliefs that will last a long time.

Ⓓ treasures and memories from childhood.

22 The phrase "With wing-heeled shoes like Mercury" in stanza 3 means to be able to —

Ⓐ be strong.

Ⓑ move fast.

Ⓒ think clearly.

Ⓓ speak rapidly.

23 What are the main differences in the themes of the poem "I Want to Fly" and the story "Doing What Comes Naturally"?

GO ON

Reading

Directions: Read the letter. Then answer the questions about the letter.

1   September 24, 1940

2   Dear Monsieur Laval,

3   Thank you for letting me visit the cave your students found just a few days ago. I am glad they shared their secret with the world. The study of prehistoric art has been my life's work. I was very happy to be one of the first people invited to see the cave.

4   In my opinion, the art in the cave was created thousands of years ago, during the Stone Age. That was before humans had developed metal tools. The Lascaux cave is the most remarkable example of Stone Age art that I have ever seen!

5   You warned me that entering the cave would be difficult. You were right. I did not enjoy squeezing through that hole. Perhaps you could make the entrance larger. The scree near the entrance will have to be sorted at some point. Piles of loose stones like that often hide small items such as broken tools. Anything we find will help us better understand those ancient people.

6   Among the hundreds of paintings, carvings, and drawings in the cave, there is some very fine art! I especially liked the way they painted groups of horses and other animals to seem like they are moving! I was also struck by the two bison bulls painted in one of the chambers of the cave. They are facing away from each other, but special shadowing with the paint shows that one is standing in front of the other. The artwork at Lascaux was done by very skilled artists.

GO ON

Reading

7   The art in this newly found cave is well organized. I noted a repeating pattern in several of the chambers, grouping together horses, bulls, and deer. Scientists think that the art of ancient people has to do with their hunting. Perhaps the art in the Lascaux cave will help prove this.

8   I will return to Lascaux as soon as possible to learn more. I will make drawings and tracings and take photographs. It will take years to catalog all the images in the cave.

9   This is the discovery of a lifetime!

10   With my very best wishes,
Henri Breuil

---

24 What is most likely the reason Monsieur Laval invited Henri Breuil to see the cave?

Ⓐ Breuil was an expert on ancient art.

Ⓑ Breuil was a friend who lived nearby.

Ⓒ Breuil could climb down into the cave.

Ⓓ Breuil knew the students who found the cave.

25 According to the letter, what is one possible reason for the art in the cave?

Ⓐ The art was related to hunting.

Ⓑ Artists made it to show off their skills.

Ⓒ The art was created thousands of years ago.

Ⓓ People lived in the cave and wanted to decorate it.

26 Why does Breuil think that the pile of stones should be sorted?

Ⓐ to protect the art from damage

Ⓑ to see if there is art underneath

Ⓒ to keep people from tripping on it

Ⓓ to find clues about the ancient people

27 Which detail best supports the idea that the Lascaux artists were highly skilled?

Ⓐ They left broken tools behind in the cave.

Ⓑ They painted the same kind of animals together.

Ⓒ They painted animals that looked like they were moving.

Ⓓ They made carvings, drawings, and paintings in the cave.

GO ON

45

Reading

28 What is the main idea of the letter?

Ⓐ A scientist came to repair prehistoric tools.

Ⓑ A scientist helped organize art found in a cave.

Ⓒ A scientist wanted to arrange a visit to a secret cave.

Ⓓ A scientist was grateful to study examples of prehistoric art.

29 How is the information in this letter organized?

Ⓐ Details are compared and contrasted.

Ⓑ A problem and its solution are described.

Ⓒ Details about each topic are grouped together.

Ⓓ Events are listed in the order in which they happened.

30 Read this sentence from paragraph 1.

> I am glad they shared their secret with the world.

Which of these words is most nearly the **opposite** of shared, as it is used in this sentence?

Ⓐ hid

Ⓑ told

Ⓒ made

Ⓓ changed

31 Read this sentence from paragraph 1.

> The study of prehistoric art has been my life's work.

The word prehistoric includes the Latin prefix *pre-*, so the word prehistoric probably means something that happened —

Ⓐ before written history.

Ⓑ during written history.

Ⓒ after written history.

32 Read this sentence from paragraph 1.

> I was very happy to be one of the first people invited to see the cave.

Which word could replace happy in this sentence to show that Henri Breuil is both happy and excited?

Ⓐ glad

Ⓑ thrilled

Ⓒ amused

Ⓓ pleased

33 In paragraph 8, the phrase "to catalog all the images" means to —

Ⓐ improve them.

Ⓑ tell about them.

Ⓒ make a list of them.

Ⓓ put a price on them.

GO ON

Reading

Directions: Read the article. Then answer the questions about the article.

Ancient Art

1   We expect to see art in museums, but some art is in surprising places. It is in caves! One of the most famous caves with prehistoric art is in Lascaux, France. The art in the Lascaux (pronounced La•**skow**) cave was created before there were machines or cities or farms, and before people invented writing. No one knows why ancient people made these images. Perhaps it was their way of sending a "letter" to the future.

2   The art in Lascaux mostly shows animals, such as horses, oxen, deer, bears, lions, and mammoths. Some of the animals, like mammoths, have all died off and are extinct now. Mammoths were like elephants with long hair and huge tusks. Lions are still living but are not found in Europe.

3   Not all of the Lascaux art shows animals. There is one drawing of a person. Also, there are symbols, like lines and dots and shapes. The meaning of the symbols is unknown.

4   The Lascaux cave has three kinds of art. Most of the art was carved into the walls of the cave. Ancient artists used tools made of stone or animal bone to do the carving. The two other kinds of art are drawings and paintings. The artists made their paint from colorful rocks and clay, creating black, brown, red, yellow, and white. Sometimes they did "spray painting" by blowing the paint through a tube onto the cave wall. Scientists found hollowed-out animal bones with paint stains inside them.

GO ON

47

Reading

5   The Lascaux art was unseen for thousands of years. Then, in 1940, four teenage boys wiggled through a hole in the ground and found themselves inside the cave. They were amazed to see pictures of animals all over the cave walls. They kept it a secret for a few days, and then told their teacher, Mr. Laval. Curious visitors came to see the wonderful art, including Henri Breuil, an expert in prehistoric cave art. Then many more people came to see the Lascaux cave. Over the years, so many people visited the cave that their breath caused mold to grow on the paintings. The ancient art was in danger of disappearing.

6   In 1963, to preserve the art, the cave was closed to all visitors except a few scientists. But the French government kindly built a copy of the Lascaux cave, called Lascaux II, right next to the real one. Visitors can now visit Lascaux II. Scholars are still interested in the Lascaux cave. They are trying to learn more about the ancient art and the people who created it. The meaning of the art is still a mystery.

---

34 Which detail best supports the idea that animals were important to the Lascaux artists?

Ⓐ Three different types of art were used in the cave.

Ⓑ Most of the images in the cave are of animals.

Ⓒ The animals are painted with certain colors.

Ⓓ The images were created a long time ago.

35 What is one reason the art in Lascaux cave is still a mystery?

Ⓐ It is not in a museum like most art.

Ⓑ People are not allowed to visit the real cave.

Ⓒ People do not know what the symbols mean.

Ⓓ It shows animals that do not live in the area.

GO ON ➡

Reading

36 Which detail best supports the idea that the cave art at Lascaux is ancient?

Ⓐ There is only one drawing of a person.

Ⓑ The art shows horses, oxen, and deer.

Ⓒ Some paintings were made by spraying paint.

Ⓓ The artists used tools made of stone and bone.

37 The different colors of paint used at Lascaux came from —

Ⓐ rocks and clay.

Ⓑ carving on the walls.

Ⓒ ground animal bones.

Ⓓ blowing through bone tubes.

38 What reason does the author give for why the Lascaux cave was closed?

Ⓐ People were worried someone would fall.

Ⓑ Visitors were causing mold to grow in the cave.

Ⓒ The air in the cave was hard for people to breathe.

Ⓓ The cave was too crowded for people to do their work.

39 How is paragraph 5 of this article organized?

Ⓐ A cause and its effects are explained.

Ⓑ Events are described in the order in which they happen.

Ⓒ Details are listed in the order of their importance.

Ⓓ A problem and its solution are described.

GO ON

Reading

40 In paragraph 2, the word <u>extinct</u> means that mammoths —

Ⓐ are no longer alive.

Ⓑ are carefully protected.

Ⓒ stay away from humans.

Ⓓ are among the largest animals on Earth.

41 Read these sentences from paragraph 6.

> Scholars are still interested in the Lascaux cave. They are trying to learn more about the ancient art and the people who created it.

The word <u>scholars</u> means people who —

Ⓐ visit.

Ⓑ paint.

Ⓒ study.

Ⓓ guide.

42 Compare the article "Ancient Art" and the letter of page 44. How is the focus of each text alike or different? Use examples from both texts to support your answer.

GO ON

Name _____ Date _____

Reading

Directions: Read the passage. Then answer the questions about the passage.

Make Your Own Cave Paintings

Introduction

     Artists in ancient times made paintings on the rock walls inside caves. The paintings mostly showed animals. Artists made their own paint from clay and rocks of different colors. The long-ago artists used basic tools made of natural materials, like wood, stone, and bone. The ancient paintings are rather simple, but they are powerful. Would you like to make a cave painting?

Materials

- charcoal
- brown, red, yellow, and white pastels (chalk or oil)
- large brown paper bag
- pencil
- scissors
- thin cardboard

Steps

1. Draw an outline of an animal on the thin cardboard. Cave paintings often showed horses, oxen, or deer. Cut out the animal shape.

2. Cut the bag into a large piece of brown paper. Tear the edges all the way around to make them ragged and uneven. Wrinkle the paper several times so that it looks kind of like a bumpy rock wall.

3. On the brown paper, draw around your cardboard animal shape with the charcoal. Then put the cardboard shape aside.

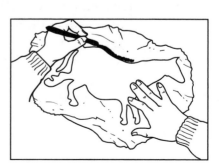

4. Blend the edges of the charcoal line using your finger. Add more charcoal if you need to. You want a thick line.

GO ON

Reading

5. Wipe your dirty fingers on parts of your paper, leaving charcoal smudges. Add some more smudges to other spots. Cave walls often had black streaks from the smoky torches that artists used for light.

6. Fill in your charcoal outline with your pastels. Some cave animals are densely painted with just one color. Others are shaded with darker and lighter color, or they have more than one color.

7. Add more animals to your paper. You may use the same cardboard shape or cut out another animal shape to use. It is okay if the lines of one animal partly cover another. Animals in cave art overlap, too.

8. Sign your work! Prehistoric artists often made handprints near their cave art. Draw around your hand with the charcoal or the pastels. Since cave paintings were usually created in layers, it is all right if your handprint signature overlaps an animal shape. Have fun!

---

43 What is the main idea of this passage?

Ⓐ Modern art is better than ancient cave paintings.

Ⓑ Ancient cave paintings were simple and easy to make.

Ⓒ Ancient cave paintings were made by tracing outlines.

Ⓓ Students can make art that looks like ancient cave paintings.

44 Which detail best supports the idea that ancient artists used basic tools?

Ⓐ Artists made handprints near their art.

Ⓑ Cave paintings were usually created in layers.

Ⓒ Cave paintings often showed horses, oxen, or deer.

Ⓓ Artists used wood, stone, and bone to help them paint.

Reading

45 Why do the directions tell students to wipe their dirty fingers on the paper?

Ⓐ It will encourage the students to make a thick line.

Ⓑ The dirty fingerprints are a way of signing the painting.

Ⓒ The dirty spots will look like streaks from ancient torches.

Ⓓ It will keep the students from getting charcoal on their clothing.

46 The author suggests tearing and wrinkling the paper in order to make it —

Ⓐ look more like a rock wall.

Ⓑ easier to blend the charcoal.

Ⓒ soft for drawing with the pastels.

Ⓓ be the right shape for the animal outline.

47 The directions tell students to draw around their hands because —

Ⓐ it helps to blend the charcoal lines.

Ⓑ handprints go well with the charcoal finger marks.

Ⓒ real cave paintings often have handprints next to them.

Ⓓ drawing around hands is an easy way to make an outline.

48 How is "Make Your Own Cave Paintings" organized?

Ⓐ Important information is given first.

Ⓑ Information is grouped into sections.

Ⓒ An idea is described and examples are listed.

Ⓓ Events are described in the order in which they happened.

GO ON

Reading

49 How is the information organized in the directions section?

Ⓐ Ideas are compared and contrasted.

Ⓑ A cause and its effects are explained.

Ⓒ A problem and its answers are described.

Ⓓ Steps are listed in the order in which students should do them.

50 Read this sentence from the introduction.

> The long-ago artists used basic tools made of natural materials, like wood, stone, and bone.

The phrase <u>natural materials</u> means the tools are made from things that —

Ⓐ are found in nature.

Ⓑ are expensive.

Ⓒ are fun to use.

Ⓓ are pretty.

51 How did ancient people make cave art like the art found in Lascaux cave? Use information from both "Ancient Art" and "Make Your Own Cave Paintings" to support your answer.

Score

_____ /56

Benchmark Writing Test

Description

The Form B Benchmark Writing Test contains 16 items. Students will respond to both multiple-choice and constructed-response items to assess Writing and Language skills.

Administering the Test

The approximate testing time for this test is 90 minutes. However, the Benchmark Assessments are not timed, so you have the flexibility to lengthen or shorten the testing times. If you wish to split testing into two sessions, end the first session after students complete item 13 (the first draft for the research prompt).

Online Administration:

- Follow the directions in eAssessment.

Print Administration:

- Make one copy of the test for each student.

- Distribute one copy of the test to each student. Have the students write their name and the date on the test.

- Make sure that students have additional paper to prepare for and write first and final drafts for the test questions that require a student-written response.

Both Administrations:

- Explain that the Benchmark Test will help the students know more about which Common Core State Standards they already know and which ones they need to work on.

- Remind students that some of the standards have not been taught yet. They should not worry if they do not know all the answers.

- If students have questions about the directions, you may read or paraphrase as necessary to make sure the students understand what to do. If students have difficulty reading the items or provided sources, you may read as necessary.

- Tell the students the approximate amount of time they will have to complete their test.

- Students may not use their books during the test. They may use a dictionary when responding to writing prompts, but it may not be used for the multiple-choice items.

NOTE: Writing Standard 6 in the Common Core State Standards assesses students' use of computer technology to produce or publish writing. If you wish to assess this standard, have students take the test in eAssessment. Alternatively, if you are using the print version, you may have students use a word processor to respond to the writing prompts.

Writing

Directions: Read the paragraph. Then answer the questions.

---

(1) This is the classroom _____ I went to kindergarten. (2) There are the same red small chairs and tables. (3) They seem so little now! (4) I _____ remember that they didn't seem little then, though. (5) My favorite activity in kindergarten was finger painting, although I loved feeding the class rabbit, _____. (6) When art time came around, I would sit quietly _____. (7) I waited for the teacher to say Okay, you may put on your aprons and go get your paints. (8) How I loved to get my fingers into the wet, gooey colors and spread them all over the paper! (9) I still like to paint, although now I usually prefer a brush.

---

1 Which answer correctly completes sentence 1?

  Ⓐ why

  Ⓑ when

  Ⓒ which

  Ⓓ where

2 What is the correct way to write sentence 2?

  Ⓐ There are the same small red chairs and tables.

  Ⓑ There is the same red small chairs and tables.

  Ⓒ There are the same red small chairs or tables.

  Ⓓ Correct as is

GO ON

Writing

3 Which answer correctly completes sentence 4?

Ⓐ can

Ⓑ will

Ⓒ may

Ⓓ would

4 Which answer correctly completes sentence 5?

Ⓐ to

Ⓑ too

Ⓒ two

5 Which answer correctly completes sentence 6?

Ⓐ at my desk

Ⓑ in very excited

Ⓒ about painting soon

Ⓓ for wait for the teacher

6 What is the correct way to write sentence 7?

Ⓐ I waited for the teacher to say "Okay, you may put on your aprons and go get your paints".

Ⓑ I waiting for the teacher to say Okay, you may put on your aprons and go get your paints.

Ⓒ I waited for the teacher to say, "Okay, you may put on your aprons and go get your paints."

Ⓓ Correct as is

GO ON

Writing

Directions: Read the paragraph. Then answer the questions.

> (1) Susan is a young tall woman who wants to become a professional athlete. (2) When Susan _____ in a race, all she tries to think about is the race! (3) Her mind _____ start to wander sometimes, but she always brings it back to the race. (4) She stays focused, she thinks only about her next step. (5) Susan is training for a big, big race now. (6) Next year, she wants to run in the New York City Marathon! (7) She knows this will be hard for her. (8) A marathon is just over 26 miles and the runners in New York are among the best in the world. (9) But Susan is confident. (10) She thinks that anything is possible if she works hard enough.

7 What is the correct way to write sentence 1?

Ⓐ Susan is a tall young woman who wants to become a professional athlete.

Ⓑ Susan is a young tall woman who want to become a professional athlete.

Ⓒ Susan is a young tall woman who wants to become a Professional Athlete.

Ⓓ Correct as is

8 Which answer correctly completes sentence 2?

Ⓐ is run

Ⓑ running

Ⓒ is running

Ⓓ be running

GO ON

Writing

9 Which answer correctly completes sentence 3?

Ⓐ do

Ⓑ may

Ⓒ must

Ⓓ should

10 What is the correct way to write sentence 4?

Ⓐ She stays focused. She thinks only about her next step.

Ⓑ She stays focused she thinks only about her next step.

Ⓒ She thinks only about her next step, she stays focused.

Ⓓ Correct as is

11 What is the correct way to write sentence 6?

Ⓐ Next year, she wants to run in the New York city Marathon!

Ⓑ Next Year, she wants to run in the New York City Marathon!

Ⓒ Next year, she want to run in the New York City Marathon!

Ⓓ Correct as is

12 What is the correct way to write sentence 8?

Ⓐ A marathon are just over 26 miles and the runners in New York are among the best in the world.

Ⓑ A marathon is just over 26 miles and the runners in New York are among the bestest in the world.

Ⓒ A marathon is just over 26 miles, and the runners in New York are among the best in the world.

Ⓓ Correct as is

GO ON

Writing

13 Your school is having a fair in which students will share how to make things. You are going to write a report about how to make and personalize a skateboard. First, read Source 1 and Source 2. Then take notes and plan your writing. You may use a graphic organizer like the one on the next page to organize your thoughts. Then, on a separate sheet of paper, write your rough draft.

Source 1

from *How Stuff Gets Made* by LeAnn Kendel. San Francisco: Hands On Press, 2010

How to Make Your Own Skateboard

by LeAnn Kendel

The process of making a skateboard is pretty simple. First, you make the **deck**. This is the part you ride on. To start the deck, you glue together eight layers of very thin wood. Then you take the layered stack of wood and press it against a curved mold. Using an old deck is ideal to give your new deck the right shape.

After the glue has dried, you will have a curved piece of wood. Have an adult help you cut and smooth the edges into the shape of a skateboard. Now spray on a few coats of paint.

Next you need to add **grip tape.** This provides a "sticky" surface to the top side of the skateboard. The last step is to screw on the **trucks** and **wheels**. The trucks are the metal axles that hold the wheels. You can buy both the trucks and the wheels at a local skate shop.

GO ON

Writing

Source 2

www.rideon.com/graphics

Personalizing Your Board

Below are two ways to personalize the underside of your board. With either one, start by taking off the trucks and the wheels.

Transfer a Drawing

If your deck, or board, is a light color, it's pretty easy to add your own design. Draw your design on a piece of paper. Transfer the design to the bottom of your deck with transfer paper. Then go over the lines with a black marker. You can also use colored paint pens.

Create a Design with Masking Tape

This method works well if your deck is a darker color. Start by sanding the bottom of your deck. Spray-paint the bottom of the deck with a light color. After the paint dries, create a design with masking tape on top of the new paint. Then paint over the masking tape using a different color. After the paint dries, peel up the tape to reveal your design.

Graphic Organizer

Sequence Chain

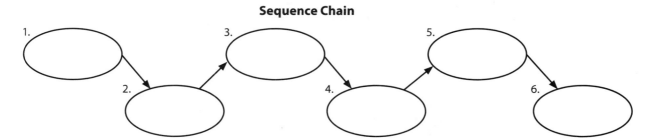

GO ON

Writing

14 Write the final version of your report about how to make a skateboard on a separate sheet of paper. Before you write, you may

- read the sources, your notes, and the graphic organizer

- review and revise your rough draft.

15 Read the poem below. Then write an essay explaining what you think the speaker of the poem is feeling and why. Cite specific evidence from the poem to support your explanation. Do your writing on a separate sheet of paper.

Spring Rain

Underground at night outside,
seeds don't sleep or even hide.
Gentle rain finds them out,
makes them swell, grow, and sprout.

Muffled sounds of late-night rain
have inspired my tired brain.
Imagination then makes roots,
new ideas send out shoots.

In a jungle I explore
animals and trees galore!
I wake with pictures in my head
but find that I am still in bed!

GO ON

Writing

16 Some parents believe students have too much homework. Other parents believe students have too little. What do you think about the amount of homework assigned? Write a letter to your principal telling your opinion about the right amount of homework. Support your opinion by explaining the effects of too much or too little homework. Do your writing on a separate sheet of paper.

Score	
_____/12 multiple-choice	
_____/4 research and draft	
_____/24 expository prompt	
_____/24 literary response prompt	
_____/24 opinion prompt	

DONE!

Benchmark Reading Test, Form C, Copy Masters	66–88

Benchmark Reading Test

Description

The Form C Benchmark Reading Test contains 52 items. Students will respond to both multiple-choice and constructed-response items to assess Reading and Vocabulary skills.

Administering the Test

The approximate testing time for this test is 90 minutes. However, the Benchmark Assessments are not timed, so you have the flexibility to lengthen or shorten the testing times. If you wish to split testing into two sessions, end the first session at the end of Page 77.

Online Administration:

- Follow the directions in eAssessment.

Print Administration:

- Make one copy of the test for each student.

- Distribute one copy of the test to each student. Have the students write their name and the date on the test.

- Make sure that students have additional paper to respond to test questions that require a student-written response.

Both Administrations:

- Explain that the Benchmark Test will help the students know more about which Common Core State Standards they already know and which ones they need to work on.

- Remind students that some of the standards have not been taught yet. They should not worry if they do not know all the answers.

- If students have questions about the directions, you may read or paraphrase as necessary to make sure the students understand what to do.

- Tell the students the approximate amount of time they will have to complete their test.

Reading

Directions: Read the play. Then answer the questions about the play.

Is the Grass Greener on the Other Side of the Fence?

1   CHARACTERS:

ULLA, a white and brown cow

ELSIE, a white and black cow

2   COSTUMES: *The costume for each cow is a spotted suit and a furry hat with big ears.* ELSIE *wears a cowbell around her neck.*

3   **ACT ONE**

SETTING: *A dairy farm. The foreground is a pasture (clumps of grass) with a red barn to one side. The painted backdrop shows a fence with a hole in it, and a road and a forest beyond the fence.* ULLA *stands near the barn.*

4   ULLA [*talks to herself*]: It's a beautiful day for grazing. And for dreaming, like Odysseus. I wonder what life would be like in faraway places.

5   [ULLA *reaches down and grabs some grass. She puts it in her mouth and chews. There is a clanging of a bell offstage.* ELSIE *enters, with the bell clanging around her neck.*]

6   ELSIE: Hey, Ulla. How are you this morning?

7   ULLA: Hi, Elsie. I'm fine, but I feel like exploring. I want to venture far and wide. I want to go through that fence [*she nods her head toward the backdrop*], across the road, through the woods, and into a whole new world. The grass there will be greener and fresher, as though it has just pushed its way up through the earth. It will taste delicious.

Reading

8   ELSIE [*looks worried*]: You're an adventurous cow, Ulla, but it's better to stay here in our own pasture. We don't know what kind of danger lurks out there beyond the fence.

9   ULLA [*rolls her eyes*]: Oh, Elsie. You're such a bore. I'm going. If you were a real friend you would come with me. [ULLA *walks toward the fence.*]

10   ELSIE [*in a pleading voice*]: I **am** a real friend, Ulla, and I beg you not to go.

11   [ULLA *continues to walk toward the fence.*]

12   ELSIE: Be careful out there....

13   **ACT TWO**
SETTING: *A forest with trees, rocks, and a stream.* ULLA *is by the stream.*

14   ULLA [*looks around in awe*]: Everything is magical, just as I imagined. There is no green grass, but there are beautiful leaves and rocks. And this bubbling stream looks like a silver ribbon. [*She takes a drink from the stream and laughs.*]

15   ULLA: It tickles! And it tastes so cool and clean, like the water in our trough just after a rainstorm.

16   [*The lights dim. There is a rumbling sound.*]

17   ULLA [*grabs her stomach*]: Oh my! My stomach is rumbling. I'm getting hungry. When you have four parts to your stomach, you've got to eat a lot. I guess I'd better head back home. [*She looks around, hesitates, and gets a worried look on her face.*]

GO ON

Reading

18   ULLA [*with a panicked voice; speaking faster and faster*]: I have no idea
         where I am! Which way is home? I'm lost. Very lost. Oh dear, I'll never
         find my friends again or my cozy barn and fresh hay to sleep in. [*A
         cowbell clangs offstage.* ULLA *turns toward the bell and smiles.*]

19   ULLA: That's Elsie! I've been saved by the bell. I only have to walk toward
         the clang and I'll be home soon, safe and sound.

---

1 In Act 1, Ulla feels that Elsie is —

  Ⓐ lost.

  Ⓑ boring.

  Ⓒ jealous.

  Ⓓ adventurous.

2 What does Ulla find across the road?

  Ⓐ a cozy barn

  Ⓑ a little home

  Ⓒ a forest with a stream

  Ⓓ a pasture with fresh grass

3 What saves Ulla from a bad end to her adventure?

  Ⓐ a kind farmer

  Ⓑ a clanging bell

  Ⓒ a hole in the fence

  Ⓓ a familiar path through the woods

4 What is the theme of the play?

  Ⓐ The best adventures are shared with friends.

  Ⓑ There is no greater danger than to lead a boring life.

  Ⓒ It's good to have a best friend to keep you out of danger.

  Ⓓ It's fun to be adventurous, but there's no place like home.

GO ON

Reading

5 Which of these sentences from the story gives the best clue to Ulla's character?

Ⓐ I beg you not to go.

Ⓑ It will taste delicious.

Ⓒ How are you this morning?

Ⓓ I want to venture far and wide.

6 What does the word <u>backdrop</u> mean in paragraph 3?

Ⓐ a style of barn

Ⓑ a type of pasture with clumps of grass

Ⓒ a background painted with a scene for a play

Ⓓ a kind of sound effect used at the back of the stage for drama

7 What does "dreaming, like Odysseus" mean in paragraph 4?

Ⓐ wanting to be the leader of a group

Ⓑ thinking about adventures in faraway places

Ⓒ deciding how to find enough food for the winter

Ⓓ imagining how to win a war and take over a land

8 In Paragraph 14, what does Ulla mean when she says the "stream looks like a silver ribbon"?

Ⓐ The stream is overflowing.

Ⓑ The stream is shiny and winding.

Ⓒ The stream is reflecting the trees.

Ⓓ The stream is as quiet as a puddle.

GO ON

Reading

Directions: Read the passage. Then answer the questions about the passage.

Is the Grass Greener on the Other Side of the Fence?

1   Ulla stood ankle deep in grass and looked out over the pasture. She liked to spend time each morning staring out into the field, imagining what life might be like in places she had never seen before. She had heard the farmers' children talking about faraway places, like the sunny beaches of Florida and the misty mountains of Tennessee. She stretched out her neck, lowered her head, and grabbed another bunch of grass. Her dreaming continued, accompanied by the rhythm of her own chewing.

2   "Hey, Ulla," said her friend Elsie. "How are you this fine morning?" Elsie wasn't very good at sneaking up on the other cows in the herd. They could always hear the loud cowbell that was around her neck. It clanged when she walked, as her bulky body swayed from side to side.

3   "Hi, Elsie. I'm fine, but I feel like exploring. I want to venture far and wide. I want to go through the fence, over the road, and into a whole new world. The grass there will be greener and fresher, as though it has just pushed its way up through the earth. It will taste delicious."

4   "You're an adventurous cow, Ulla, but it's better to stay safely here in our own pasture. We don't know what kind of danger lurks out there beyond the fence. You might be miserable."

5   "Oh, Elsie. You're such a bore. I'm going. If you were a real friend you would come with me."

Reading

6   "I *am* a real friend, Ulla, and I beg you not to go."

7   Ulla barely heard Elsie's last words. She was lumbering off toward the open hole in the fence.

8   "Be careful out there," Elsie whispered, but her voice was lost to the wind.

9   Ulla went through the hole in the fence, across the road, and through the woods. She didn't find any fresh, new grass, but she saw things she had never seen before. She looked in awe at the trees and the rocks and the bubbling stream. She took a sip of water and laughed when the rushing water tickled her nose.

10   Finally, it got dark, and the four parts of her stomach rumbled with hunger. She looked around to find her way back home, but she was lost. Nothing looked familiar. She began to panic. Which way should she go?

11   She began to wish for her friends and her warm and safe barn. But she knew she may never find these precious things again.

12   Suddenly she heard a sound in the distance. She turned and walked toward the faint clanging. As she got closer, she smiled. It was the sound of Elsie's cowbell. Home sweet home.

GO ON

Reading

9 At the very beginning of the story, why does Ulla want to travel?

Ⓐ She desires to meet new friends.

Ⓑ She would like to find food for the winter.

Ⓒ She wants to see new places and things.

Ⓓ She wishes to get away from the farmer's children.

10 What happens to make Ulla want to go back home?

Ⓐ A storm begins.

Ⓑ It gets dark and she gets hungry.

Ⓒ Elsie is calling her to come back home.

Ⓓ There are dangerous animals in the forest.

11 What sentence gives the best clue to Elsie's character?

Ⓐ If you were a real friend you would come with me.

Ⓑ She turned and walked toward the faint clanging.

Ⓒ She liked to spend time each morning staring out into the field.

Ⓓ We don't know what kind of danger lurks out there beyond the fence.

12 Which of these sentences best summarizes the story?

Ⓐ A cow has a fight with her best friend and decides to run away to find new friends.

Ⓑ Two cows think the grass in their pasture is not that tasty, so they set out to find a new grassland.

Ⓒ A cow wants to see more of the world and finds some wondrous new things, but she also wants to come back to her home and her friends.

Ⓓ Two cows talk about how boring life is in their pasture and how they wish they could see beaches and mountains.

13 In paragraph 9, what is the meaning of "She looked in awe at the trees and the rocks and the bubbling stream"?

Ⓐ She was bored by the forest.

Ⓑ She thought she was dreaming.

Ⓒ She was amazed by all these new things.

Ⓓ She was disappointed that no grass was growing.

GO ON

Reading

14 What does the word <u>miserable</u> mean in paragraph 4?

Ⓐ unhappy

Ⓑ angry

Ⓒ crazy

Ⓓ lost

15 What is the **opposite** of the word <u>familiar</u> in paragraph 10?

Ⓐ simple

Ⓑ known

Ⓒ strange

Ⓓ dreadful

---

16 Which part of the story does the illustration show? Describe how the illustration reflects the descriptions in the text.

Reading

Directions: Read the story. Then answer the questions about the story.

The Gift of Mattu Pongal

1   Ramesh rubbed his eyes sleepily and peeked out from his bed covers. Something stared back at him. He rubbed his eyes again. Every morning for the past week, the same cow had poked her head in his open window. What did she want?

2   Ramesh was always a little grumpy when he woke up, but he got grumpier when he saw the cow. "Go away!" he shouted. "I don't want your gigantic face in my window." She let out a mournful moo, and continued chewing. He jumped out of bed, waving his arms. "Go away," he repeated, even though he knew he had to be careful. In his country, cows were considered holy. They could do whatever they pleased, so they wandered the streets and ate what they wanted from people's gardens and porches.

3   Ramesh remembered that the festival of Mattu Pongal was next week. Everyone in India would honor the cattle during that celebration and thank them for giving milk. Everyone was also preparing a gift for the cows, to bring good luck for the year.

4   Ramesh thought for a moment. The gift he would like to give this cow was a one-way ticket out of town. If she went away forever, she would not stick her head in his window every morning. She would not wake him up with her moo as loud as a horn, nor would she watch his every move.

GO ON

Reading

5   The cow mooed again. Ramesh looked at her big eyes and her long eyelashes. Maybe he should think about this problem in a different way. "I'll give her a name," he said to himself. "How about Asha? That means *hope*. I HOPE she'll go away," he laughed to himself. "No, not really. I do hope, though, she'll let me sleep in now and then."

6   Ramesh spent the next few days making a beautiful necklace of flowers for Asha. This would be his gift to her for Mattu Pongal. He went to the market and chose flowers of the brightest colors he could find—red and yellow and pink. Then he laced them together with strong thread.

7   On the morning of Mattu Pongal, there was a loud "moo" as usual. However, this special morning, Ramesh did not shout or wave his hands. Instead, he helped his father wash Asha and paint her horns. Then he tenderly put the flowers around her neck. Now she was ready for the festival. And Ramesh and his family were ready for a year of good luck. "Every cloud has a silver lining," Ramesh thought to himself.

8   Asha lifted her head like a queen. She looked right at Ramesh and blinked. He was sure it was a cow's way of winking, so he smiled and winked back.

---

17 Where does Ramesh first meet the cow?

Ⓐ at the town festival

Ⓑ in the flower market

Ⓒ at his bedroom window

Ⓓ in the family dining room

18 What detail from the story shows that Ramesh gets grumpier than usual when he sees the cow?

Ⓐ He rubs his eyes sleepily.

Ⓑ He yells and waves his arms.

Ⓒ He says he needs more sleep.

Ⓓ He peeks out from his bed covers.

GO ON

Reading

19 What does "Every cloud has a silver lining" mean in paragraph 7?

   Ⓐ There are many storms in life.

   Ⓑ A bad situation can have a good ending.

   Ⓒ It is useful to save money when you can.

   Ⓓ When you need rain, just look to the skies for help.

20 Why does Ramesh change his feelings toward the cow?

   Ⓐ She starts to watch him.

   Ⓑ She stops waking him up.

   Ⓒ He sees something friendly in her big eyes.

   Ⓓ He knows she can provide milk for the family.

21 Which of these best summarizes the story?

   Ⓐ A boy thinks he will get in trouble for having a cow in his room.

   Ⓑ A cow wanders into a boy's house and starts to eat things she finds in his room.

   Ⓒ A country plans a festival to honor cattle, and everyone makes gifts to celebrate.

   Ⓓ A boy decides to make the best of a difficult situation and ends up with a new friend.

22 What does Ramesh do to get ready for the festival of Mattu Pongal?

   Ⓐ He scares the cow away.

   Ⓑ He plants garden flowers.

   Ⓒ He makes a colorful necklace.

   Ⓓ He makes his bed and cleans his room.

23 What does the gift of "a one-way ticket out of town" mean in paragraph 4?

   Ⓐ Ramesh does not like to give gifts.

   Ⓑ Ramesh does not want the cow to come back.

   Ⓒ Ramesh wants to go on vacation with his family.

   Ⓓ Ramesh wants to let the cow wander because she is holy.

GO ON

Reading

24 Review the dictionary entries below.

stick (**stik**) *noun* **1** a part of a tree **2** a long piece of wood or metal **3** a tool used for striking an object in a game **4** a lever to operate something

stick (**stik**) *verb* **1** to pierce something or put a hole through something **2** to put something in place or position **3** to attach something to a surface

What is the meaning of the word <u>stick</u> in paragraph 4?

(A) a long piece of wood or metal

(B) to put something in position

(C) to put a hole in something

(D) a part of a tree

---

25 How are the plots in the stories "The Gift of Mattu Pongal" and "Is the Grass Greener on the Other Side of the Fence?" different? Think about what happens in the beginning, middle, and end of each story.

GO ON

Reading

Directions: Read the article. Then answer the questions about the article.

Dolphin Rescue

1   Dolphins are very intelligent animals. They communicate in many ways. They squeak, whistle, and slap their tails on the water. This tells other dolphins about food or danger. A dolphin makes loud clicking sounds that travel in the water. When the sounds hit an object like a rock or a fish, an echo bounces back. The echoes give the dolphin information, such as how big or how far away something is.

2   But there is a great mystery about dolphins. Early in 2012, over 80 dolphins beached themselves at Cape Cod, Massachusetts. Being stranded on the sand is very dangerous for a dolphin. Usually, it breathes through a blowhole on top of its body. But when it is beached, the weight of its body cuts off its breathing.

3   Luckily, people want to help dolphins. The International Fund for Animal Welfare (IFAW) has hundreds of volunteers to help with dolphin emergencies. The best thing to do is to keep dolphins from ever getting to the beach. One way is to keep a boat between a group of dolphins and the beach. Another way is for people on the shore to make loud sounds to warn dolphins away.

4   But sometimes dolphins get beached anyway, like the ones in early 2012 at Cape Cod. It was time for humans to get to work. First, the dolphins had to be moved onto long stretchers and covered with blankets. Then volunteers had to carry the stretchers to rescue trucks. This did not happen quickly. A dolphin can weigh hundreds of pounds. It may take anywhere from two to nine people to carry one, depending on its size.

Reading

5   The rescue trucks drove the dolphins to a medical center, where they were cared for by experts. The dolphins that were okay were released back into the sea. But first, a tracking device was put on each one. This will help scientists learn more about dolphins' swimming behavior.

6   The mystery remains: Why do dolphins swim ashore? It's possible the dolphins at Cape Cod were following a dolphin that had lost its way. It might be they were chasing fish and lost track of where they were. Or maybe they got beached because they had trouble finding their way out of the U-shaped bay of Cape Cod. They may have thought they were in the open sea. Maybe they did not realize how close they were to the beach. No one really knows why dolphins get beached.

7   For now, the key to helping dolphins is human volunteers. A.J. Cady, who works for IFAW, says, "People can relate to these mammals . . . . They're such gentle animals, you can't help but feel sorry for them when they're stranded."

---

26 What is the main idea of this article?

Ⓐ Dolphins are smart animals that sometimes need our help.

Ⓑ Cape Cod is a dangerous place for both dolphins and humans.

Ⓒ Cape Cod needs special volunteers to help with dolphin rescue.

Ⓓ Dolphins create echoes to learn how big or how far away things are.

27 The author supports the idea that dolphins are intelligent by saying that they —

Ⓐ are mysterious.

Ⓑ can communicate.

Ⓒ depend on humans.

Ⓓ come ashore together.

GO ON

Reading

28 Which of these tells why being stranded is dangerous for a dolphin?

  Ⓐ A dolphin breathes through its blowhole.

  Ⓑ A dolphin makes sounds that travel in the water.

  Ⓒ A dolphin is too heavy to breathe outside of the water.

  Ⓓ A dolphin stranded on the beach is considered an emergency.

29 The main idea of paragraph 3 is that there are ways to keep dolphins from needing to be rescued. Which of these supports that idea?

  Ⓐ People want to help dolphins.

  Ⓑ IFAW has hundreds of volunteers.

  Ⓒ IFAW helps with dolphin emergencies.

  Ⓓ People on shore can make noise to warn dolphins away.

30 Why would volunteers keep a boat between a group of dolphins and the shore?

  Ⓐ to help the dolphins find their way out of the bay

  Ⓑ to see what kind of fish the dolphins are chasing

  Ⓒ to prevent the dolphins from swimming onto the beach

  Ⓓ to learn more about the ways that dolphins communicate

31 The tracking devices help scientists —

  Ⓐ give the dolphins better medical care.

  Ⓑ understand the sounds that dolphins make.

  Ⓒ learn about the swimming habits of dolphins.

  Ⓓ prevent the dolphins from having to be rescued again.

GO ON

Reading

32 The author includes the events in paragraph 4 to show that —

Ⓐ dolphins can be very heavy.

Ⓑ volunteers have to drive rescue trucks.

Ⓒ dolphins need to be covered with blankets.

Ⓓ volunteers work very hard to save dolphins.

33 Which of these best describes how the information in this article is organized?

Ⓐ by contrasting and comparing events

Ⓑ by presenting a problem and its solution

Ⓒ by giving a cause and showing its effects

Ⓓ by showing the order in which things happen

34 When an animal is beached, it is —

Ⓐ far from the shore.

Ⓑ stuck on the shore.

Ⓒ living along the shore.

Ⓓ swimming to the shore.

35 The word volunteers means people who —

Ⓐ are medical experts.

Ⓑ track how animals move.

Ⓒ spend their time helping others.

Ⓓ study dolphins in the wild.

GO ON

Reading

Form C

Directions: Read the article. Then answer the questions about the article.

Saving Animals' Lives

1   It is not easy for a wild animal to survive. It has to stay warm, find food, and avoid danger. Of course, this is part of the natural order of the world. What happens, though, when humans make things even harder for animals?

2   Take the seal, for example. It can be hurt by natural dangers, like sharks. But seals are also put at risk by human-made dangers, like fishing nets. Seals and other sea mammals can get tangled in fishing equipment. The animals have no defense for this. If a seal gets trapped in a net, it cannot save itself.

3   There are organizations that want to help. One of these is the International Fund for Animal Welfare (IFAW). This group will assist, or help, any animals, whether the animals are tame or wild. IFAW was started in 1969, to protect baby seals from hunters. Today, IFAW runs animal rescue projects in forty countries. It also will deal with sudden disasters anywhere.

4   In 2011, Japan suffered a huge earthquake. Thousands of people lost their homes and businesses. In emergencies like this, it is easy to forget the animals. But IFAW made plans to rescue and help Japan's wild creatures. They also helped many cats, dogs, and farm animals that needed human attention.

5   In Africa, hunters known as poachers capture big animals like elephants and hippos even though it is against the law. In 1989, IFAW started working to save these animals. One way it did this was by strengthening protections at wildlife parks. After this, elephant numbers in Uganda grew from 150 to around 5,000.

Reading

6   IFAW hires a lot of animal experts, but it also counts on volunteers. For example, at Cape Cod in Massachusetts, dolphins sometimes get stranded on shore. To be saved, the dolphins are put on stretchers. Then they are lifted onto trucks and taken to get medical care. Who does this backbreaking work? The local builders, secretaries, students, and other volunteers who live in the area.

7   Each person has his or her own reason for helping. Of course, many IFAW volunteers are animal lovers. Many of them are also people who want to be a force for good in the world. These volunteers find that saving an animal's life is a great reward.

---

36 The main idea of the article is that animals often need humans to help them survive. Which of these best supports that idea?

Ⓐ IFAW was started in 1969.

Ⓑ IFAW hires many animal experts.

Ⓒ Seals are unable to free themselves from a net.

Ⓓ Seals must stay warm, find food, and avoid danger.

37 IFAW got its start by —

Ⓐ protecting baby seals from hunters in 1969.

Ⓑ helping wild animals in Japan after the earthquake in 2011.

Ⓒ strengthening the protection at African wildlife parks in 1989.

Ⓓ raising the number of elephants living in Uganda from 150 to 2,400.

38 The number of elephants in Uganda grew from 150 to 2,400. What inference can you draw from this detail?

Ⓐ The elephants are safer.

Ⓑ The elephants are older.

Ⓒ The wildlife parks are bigger.

Ⓓ New animals were sent to the wildlife parks.

39 Which of these is the best summary of this article?

Ⓐ IFAW worked to protect elephants.

Ⓑ IFAW is a group that works to help animals in need.

Ⓒ IFAW works with animal volunteers in Massachusetts.

Ⓓ IFAW helped wild animals after an earthquake in Japan.

 GO ON

Reading

40 IFAW stands for International Fund for Animal Welfare. The word <u>International</u> means that this group —

Ⓐ works in more than one country.

Ⓑ welcomes all kinds of volunteers.

Ⓒ helps both wild and tame animals.

Ⓓ does both water and land rescues.

41 Which pair of words in paragraph 3 gives the meaning of the word <u>assist</u>?

Ⓐ forty countries

Ⓑ that want

Ⓒ will deal

Ⓓ or help

42 Read this sentence from paragraph 5.

> In Africa, hunters known as poachers capture big animals like elephants and hippos even though it is against the law.

In which of these words from the article does the suffix *-er* mean the same as it does in the word <u>hunters</u>?

Ⓐ builders

Ⓑ dangers

Ⓒ numbers

Ⓓ stretchers

43 How are the dangers faced by dolphins in "Dolphin Rescue" different from the dangers faced by seals in "Saving Animals' Lives"?

GO ON

Reading

Directions: Read the article. Then answer the questions about the article.

Hello from Earth

1   Earth is a small planet tucked away in the corner of a giant galaxy. Is there any way we can send a "hello" to the rest of the universe?

2   Yes! In fact, we already have. In 1977, the United States launched two spaceships into outer space. They were named Voyager 1 and Voyager 2. These ships had no astronauts. That's because the spacecraft were making a one-way trip into the great unknown.

3   The Voyagers had two goals. First, the ships would travel through the Solar System and beyond. Along the way, the spacecraft would collect information. This information would be sent back to Earth.

4   Second, the ships would carry our "hello" to the universe. If a different form of life discovered a Voyager, it could learn about us. That's because the ships contain lots of information. For example, the Voyagers are carrying many photographs. These pictures show what life on Earth is like. There are also recordings of greetings in 55 different languages. There is even music, like jazz and classical, on board.

5   Knowing when to send the Voyagers out into space was very important. The plan was for each spacecraft to visit four planets: Jupiter, Saturn, Uranus, and Neptune. For that to be possible, the four planets had to be lined up. They are lined up only once every 176 years! But it happened in 1977, and that's when scientists launched the two Voyager ships.

GO ON

Reading

6   Cameras on the Voyagers took photos as they went. They photographed the four planets and 48 of their moons. Lots of good photos were sent back to Earth. They gave scientists many new things to think about. For example, they took pictures of Io, which is a moon of Jupiter. The photographs showed that Io has active volcanoes! Nobody had known this before.

7   The Voyagers travel over 600 miles a minute. They have already traveled billions of miles. At this rate, Voyager 1 will leave our Solar System by 2015. Then it will be in the great empty space between our Sun and the closest star—an area called interstellar space.

8   The two Voyagers should be able to continue sending information to Earth until 2025. At that point, the spacecraft will finally lose touch with us. Maybe someday, a life form we don't know about will discover one of the Voyagers. Then the sound of our music will be heard billions of miles from Earth. Our "hello" to the universe will finally be heard!

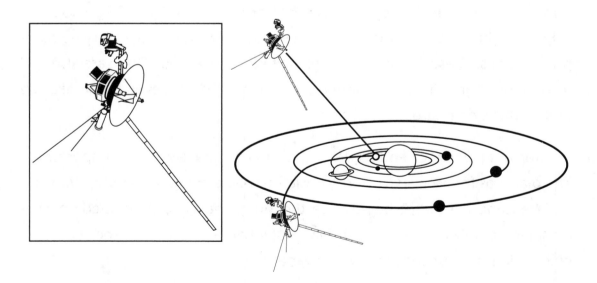

A close-up of a Voyager spacecraft and the paths of Voyager 1 and 2

GO ON

Reading

44 The Voyagers were sent as a "hello" to outer space. Which detail best supports that idea?

Ⓐ The ships take photographs as they travel.

Ⓑ The ships left with the plan to visit four planets.

Ⓒ The ships carry recordings of different greetings.

Ⓓ The ships have given scientists many things to think about.

45 Why was it important for the Voyagers to begin their travels in 1977?

Ⓐ Four planets were lined up.

Ⓑ Both ships were finally ready to go.

Ⓒ Scientists were eager to learn new things.

Ⓓ There was an active volcano in space that year.

46 Which of these is an example of how the Voyagers have been useful?

Ⓐ They travel hundreds of miles a minute.

Ⓑ They will lose touch with us after a while.

Ⓒ They showed that Io has active volcanoes.

Ⓓ They will soon be between the Sun and the closest star.

47 Which of these is the best summary of the article?

Ⓐ By 2015, the Voyagers will have traveled billions of miles in space.

Ⓑ Voyagers 1 and 2 were sent on a one-way trip without astronauts in 1977.

Ⓒ The Voyagers will send information until 2025, when they lose touch with us.

Ⓓ In 1977, Voyagers 1 and 2 were sent into space to carry and gather information.

48 Paragraphs 6, 7, and 8 of the article are organized —

Ⓐ by contrasting and comparing events.

Ⓑ by presenting a problem and its solution.

Ⓒ by giving a cause and showing its effects.

Ⓓ by showing the order in which things happen.

49 The article says that the United States launched two spaceships. The word launched means that the ships were —

Ⓐ sent into space.

Ⓑ studied by scientists.

Ⓒ filled with information.

Ⓓ owned by the government.

GO ON

Reading

50 What is a synonym for the word <u>discovered</u>, used in paragraph 4?

Ⓐ heard

Ⓑ found

Ⓒ studied

Ⓓ returned

51 Use the dictionary entry to choose the best answer.

> **point** ('point) *noun* **1** the sharp end of a tool **2** a mark or unit of scoring **3** a particular moment in time **4** a single item or detail in a list

Which meaning of <u>point</u> is used in this sentence?

> At that <u>point</u>, the spacecraft will finally lose touch with us.

Ⓐ meaning 1

Ⓑ meaning 2

Ⓒ meaning 3

Ⓓ meaning 4

52 How does the illustration on page 78 help readers understand this article?

Score

_____/56

Benchmark Writing Test, Form C, Copy Masters	90–96

Benchmark Writing Test

Description

The Form C Benchmark Writing Test contains 16 items. Students will respond to both multiple-choice and constructed-response items to assess Writing and Language skills.

Administering the Test

The approximate testing time for this test is 90 minutes. However, the Benchmark Assessments are not timed, so you have the flexibility to lengthen or shorten the testing times. If you wish to split testing into two sessions, end the first session after students complete item 13 (the first draft for the research prompt).

Online Administration:

- Follow the directions in eAssessment.

Print Administration:

- Make one copy of the test for each student.

- Distribute one copy of the test to each student. Have the students write their name and the date on the test.

- Make sure that students have additional paper to prepare for and write first and final drafts for the test questions that require a student-written response.

Both Administrations:

- Explain that the Benchmark Test will help the students know more about which Common Core State Standards they already know and which ones they need to work on.

- Remind students that some of the standards have not been taught yet. They should not worry if they do not know all the answers.

- If students have questions about the directions, you may read or paraphrase as necessary to make sure the students understand what to do. If students have difficulty reading the items or provided sources, you may read as necessary.

- Tell the students the approximate amount of time they will have to complete their test.

- Students may not use their books during the test. They may use a dictionary when responding to writing prompts, but it may not be used for the multiple-choice items.

NOTE: Writing Standard 6 in the Common Core State Standards assesses students' use of computer technology to produce or publish writing. If you wish to assess this standard, have students take the test in eAssessment. Alternatively, if you are using the print version, you may have students use a word processor to respond to the writing prompts.

Writing

Directions: Read the paragraph. Then answer the questions.

---

(1) My sister likes science, and she likes to help people. **(2)** That is _____ she wants to become a doctor. **(3)** She told my dad Believe me, I know it's not going to be easy. **(4)** She is right. **(5)** After high school, she will need _____ years of college. **(6)** Then, medical school. **(7)** _____, she will have to be an intern. **(8)** She knows she _____ many years studying and working very hard to become a doctor. **(9)** Still, she wants to do it! **(10)** She sees herself helping little children. **(11)** I admire my sister a lot. **(12)** She is ready to work hard for her dreams!

---

1 Which answer correctly completes sentence 2?

Ⓐ why

Ⓑ when

Ⓒ which

Ⓓ where

2 What is the correct way to write sentence 3?

Ⓐ "She told my dad believe me, I know it's not going to be easy."

Ⓑ She told my Dad, Believe me, I know it's not going to be easy.

Ⓒ She told my dad, "Believe me, I know it's not going to be easy."

Ⓓ Correct as is

GO ON

Writing

3 Which answer correctly completes sentence 5?

   Ⓐ for

   Ⓑ fore

   Ⓒ four

4 What is the correct way to write sentence 6?

   Ⓐ Then, go to Medical school.

   Ⓑ Then, she will go to medical school.

   Ⓒ Then, medical school after that.

   Ⓓ Correct as is

5 Which answer correctly completes sentence 7?

   Ⓐ After very difficult

   Ⓑ After study so hard

   Ⓒ After medical school

   Ⓓ After so long and hard

6 Which answer correctly completes sentence 8?

   Ⓐ do spend

   Ⓑ can spends

   Ⓒ may spends

   Ⓓ must spend

GO ON

Writing

Directions: Read the paragraph. Then answer the questions.

---

(1) Mike goes to a school where every student has to take a foreign language. **(2)** Mike _____ to speak Spanish. **(3)** His class meets three times a week. **(4)** A new teacher, mrs. Estrada, teaches it. **(5)** She likes to teach Spanish _____. **(6)** The teacher and all the kids sit around a round big table. **(7)** The teacher says something to start things off and one student responds. **(8)** Then another. **(9)** Everybody gets to talk, and the students are learning a lot. **(10)** Next week, the class is going to a Mexican restaurant. **(11)** They will all have to order in Spanish!

---

7 Which answer correctly completes sentence 2?

Ⓐ be learning

Ⓑ is learning

Ⓒ is learns

Ⓓ learning

8 What is the correct way to write sentence 4?

Ⓐ A new teacher, Mrs. Estrada, teaches it.

Ⓑ A new teacher mrs. Estrada, teaches it.

Ⓒ A new teacher, mrs. Estrada, teach it.

Ⓓ Correct as is

GO ON

Writing

9 Which answer correctly completes sentence 5?

  Ⓐ on class

  Ⓑ by speak

  Ⓒ in not difficult

  Ⓓ through talking

10 What is the correct way to write sentence 6?

  Ⓐ The teacher and all the kids sit around a round, big table.

  Ⓑ The teacher and all the kids sits around a round big table.

  Ⓒ The teacher and all the kids sit around a big round table.

  Ⓓ Correct as is

11 What is the correct way to write sentence 7?

  Ⓐ The teacher says something to start things off, one student responds.

  Ⓑ The teacher says something to start things off, and one student responds.

  Ⓒ The teacher says something to start things off and one student respond.

  Ⓓ Correct as is

12 What is the correct way to write sentence 8?

  Ⓐ Then another!

  Ⓑ Then another student responds.

  Ⓒ Then more answers from other students.

  Ⓓ Correct as is

GO ON

Writing

13 Your class is learning about the pros and cons of space travel. You are going to write an essay telling your opinion about whether sending humans into space is worthwhile. Read Source 1 and Source 2. Then take notes and plan your writing. You may use a graphic organizer like the one on the next page to organize your thoughts. Then, on a separate sheet of paper, write your rough draft.

Source 1

from the *Cape Monitor* newspaper, July 8, 2011

Final Shuttle Takes Off On Schedule

by Richard Blostov

CAPE CANAVERAL—The last mission of the Space Shuttle program left the Kennedy Space Center this morning. *Atlantis* lifted off at 11:29 a.m. This was the last of 135 missions. The Space Shuttle program started in 1981.

Over the years, the missions helped build the International Space Station. It is the most advanced orbiting laboratory in history. The shuttle commander for this mission, Chris Ferguson, said that the shuttle program showed "this great nation at its best."

The program has also had its critics. For one thing, the program turned out to be more expensive than anticipated. Each launch cost an average of $1.5 billion. At a time when the country needs schools and roads, many question the value of such an expense.

The shuttle program has also cost lives. Two of its missions ended in disaster. *Challenger*, in 1986, and *Columbia*, in 2003, lost their crews in accidents.

Writing

Form C

Source 2

www.SpaceCadets.org/US

Missions and Estimated Costs of Some Space Programs

Piloted Programs	Unpiloted Programs
International Space Station Orbiting space laboratory. Many countries cooperate to run it. *Est. Cost: $100 billion*	**Hubble Telescope** Discovered many new stars and galaxies. *Est. Cost: $10 billion*
Space Shuttle Built the International Space Station. Repaired the Hubble Telescope. *Est. Cost: $200 billion*	**Galileo** Explored Jupiter. Sent back photographs and data that helped scientists learn about it. *Est. Cost: less than $2 billion*
Apollo Landed on the moon. Inspired a generation of Americans. *Est. Cost: $170 billion*	**Cassini-Huygens** Explored Saturn and discovered 3 new moons. Sent pictures and data back to Earth. *Est. Cost: $3 billion*

Graphic Organizer

Opinion:

↓

Support 1:

Support 2:

Support 3:

↓

Conclusion:

GO ON →

Writing

14 Write the final version of your essay about space travel on a separate sheet of paper. Before you write, you may

- read the sources, your notes, and the graphic organizer
- review and revise your rough draft.

15 Write a narrative for your teacher about when you visited a place for the very first time. Do your writing on a separate sheet of paper. Be sure to

- tell what you did during your visit
- use time-order words to tell clearly when things happened
- give enough specific details so the teacher can understand what the place was like.

16 Imagine you and your classmates are making a recipe book of sandwiches to share with other classes. You are going to write detailed instructions for how to make your favorite sandwich. Do your writing on a separate sheet of paper. Be sure to

- introduce your favorite sandwich and tell why you like it
- explain what ingredients are needed
- explain exactly how to put them together to create the sandwich.

Score		
_____	/12 multiple-choice	
_____	/4 research and draft	
_____	/24 opinion prompt	
_____	/24 narrative prompt	
_____	/24 expository prompt	

Answer Keys and Rubrics

Each form of the test has two pages of Answer Keys and Rubrics to score student responses. Use the Answer Keys and Rubrics to score the students' tests. The Answer Keys also include the Common Core State Standard Code(s) for each item. See the sample Answer Keys and Rubrics page on Page T4 for more information.

The Writing Traits Rubric is an analytic scoring tool you can use to evaluate various types of student writing based on traits of good writing. Use this rubric to score the student responses for items 14–16 in the Benchmark Writing Tests.

If students have taken the tests online using eAssessment, you will need to read and assign a score to the constructed-response items and the student writing. Then follow the directions in eAssessment to record these scores.

Student Profiles

Use the Student Profiles to record student scores and report results. There are two Student Profiles, one for all three forms of the Benchmark Reading Tests and another for all forms of the Benchmark Writing Tests. The Student Profile includes the grade-level Common Core State Standards codes and text for easy reference and shows the items in the tests that are aligned with each standard. Make copies of each Student Profile for every student. See the sample Student Profiles on Pages T6 and T7 for more information.

Class Grouping Summary

Use the Class Grouping Summary to record the names or initials of students who would benefit from more instruction or practice on tasks related to each Common Core State Standard. Make a copy of each page of the Class Grouping Summary for every form. See the Sample Class Grouping Summary on Page T8 for more information.

Answer Keys and Rubrics
Benchmark Reading Test

Directions: Use the keys and rubrics below to score the test items.

Benchmark Reading Test – Form A					
Item	Key	Code	Item	Key	Code
1	A	CC.4.Rlit.3	25	C	CC.4.Rinf.2
2	D	CC.4.Rlit.3	26	C	CC.4.Rinf.3
3	A	CC.4.Rlit.1	27	D	CC.4.Rinf.1
4	C	CC.4.Rlit.2	28	B	CC.4.Rinf.2
5	B	CC.4.Rlit.1	29	A	CC.4.Rinf.5
6	C	CC.4.L.5.a	30	C	CC.4.L.4.a
7	B	CC.4.L.4.a	31	D	CC.4.Rinf.4
8	B	CC.4.Rlit.4	32	Rubric	CC.4.Rinf.7
9	C	CC.4.Rlit.1	33	D	CC.4.Rinf.2
10	B	CC.4.Rlit.3	34	C	CC.4.Rinf.1
11	C	CC.4.Rlit.4	35	C	CC.4.Rinf.3
12	A	CC.4.Rlit.1	36	C	CC.4.Rinf.2
13	B	CC.4.Rlit.3	37	D	CC.4.Rinf.8
14	A	CC.4.Rlit.3	38	D	CC.4.Rinf.5
15	D	CC.4.Rlit.2	39	A	CC.4.Rinf.4
16	B	CC.4.L.5.c	40	B	CC.4.Rinf.4
17	Rubric	CC.4.Rlit.9	41	A	CC.4.Rinf.6
18	B	CC.4.Rlit.3	42	A	CC.4.L.4.c
19	D	CC.4.Rlit.1	43	B	CC.4.Rinf.2
20	B	CC.4.Rlit.2	44	A	CC.4.Rinf.8
21	D	CC.4.L.5.b	45	C	CC.4.L.4.b
22	C	CC.4.L.6	46	D	CC.4.Rinf.3
23	C	CC.4.Rlit.4	47	D	CC.4.Rinf.4
24	Rubric	CC.4.Rlit.9	48	B	CC.4.Rinf.1
			49	A	CC.4.Rinf.2
			50	B	CC.4.L.4.c
			51	Rubric	CC.4.Rinf.6

Item 17 Rubric

Student writes a comparison that

3 points	fully describes the similarities and differences in the themes of the two stories.
2 points	partially describes the similarities and differences in the themes of the two stories.
1 point	is minimal and/or incorrect.

Item 24 Rubric

Student writes a comparison that

3 points	fully describes the similarities and differences in the ways the characters in the two stories change.
2 points	partially describes the similarities and differences in the ways the characters in the two stories change.
1 point	is minimal and/or incorrect.

Item 32 Rubric

Student writes an explanation that

2 points	fully describes how the timeline aids in understanding the passage.
1 point	is partial and/or incorrect.

Item 51 Rubric

Student writes a comparison that

3 points	fully describes how the first- or secondhand viewpoint affects the presentation of information in two passages on the same topic.
2 points	partially describes how the first- or secondhand viewpoint affects the presentation of information in two passages on the same topic.
1 point	is minimal and/or incorrect.

Scoring Note: Assign zero points if a student provides no response or an unscorable response.

Answer Keys and Rubrics
Benchmark Writing Test

Directions: Use the keys below to score the multiple-choice test items. Use the Skill Rubric on this page and the Writing Traits Rubric on page 104 to score the student responses to the writing prompts.

Benchmark Writing Test – Form A		
Item	**Key**	**Code**
1	B	CC.4.L.1.a
2	C	CC.4.L.1.b
3	D	CC.4.L.1.c
4	D	CC.4.L.1.e
5	A	CC.4.L.2.b, W.5
6	B	CC.4.L.2.g
7	A	CC.4.L.1.a
8	B	CC.4.L.2.c, W.5
9	D	CC.4.L.1.b
10	A	CC.4.L.1.d, W.5
11	D	CC.4.L.2.a
12	C	CC.4.L.1.f, W.5
13	Skill Rubric	CC.4.W.2.a, W.7, W.8, W.9.b
14	Skill Rubric	CC.4.W.2, W.4, W.5, W.7, W.8, W.9.b, L.1, L.2, L.3, L.6
15	Skill Rubric	CC.4.W.3, W.4, W.5, L.1, L.2, L.3, L.6
16	Skill Rubric	CC.4.W.1, W.4, W.5, L.1, L.2, L.3, L.6

Item 13 Skill Rubric	
Student writes a rough draft of a report that	
4 points	thoroughly incorporates the two research sources presented and makes use of notes and/or a graphic organizer.
3 points	adequately incorporates most of one or both research sources presented and makes use of notes and/or a graphic organizer.
2 points	makes some use of parts of one or both research sources presented and makes use of notes or a graphic organizer.
1 point	makes little if any use of any part of either research source presented or does not make use of any notes or a graphic organizer.

Scoring Note: Assign zero points if a student provides no response or an unscorable response.

Answer Keys and Rubrics
Benchmark Reading Test

Directions: Use the keys and rubrics below to score the test items.

Benchmark Reading Test – Form B					
Item	**Key**	**Code**	**Item**	**Key**	**Code**
1	C	CC.4.Rlit.1	24	A	CC.4.Rinf.3
2	A	CC.4.Rlit.1	25	A	CC.4.Rinf.1
3	D	CC.4.Rlit.2	26	D	CC.4.Rinf.3
4	D	CC.4.Rlit.2	27	C	CC.4.Rinf.2
5	A	CC.4.Rlit.3	28	D	CC.4.Rinf.2
6	D	CC.4.Rlit.3	29	C	CC.4.Rinf.5
7	D	CC.4.L.5.c	30	A	CC.4.L.5.c
8	A	CC.4.L.4.a	31	A	CC.4.L.4.b
9	B	CC.4.Rlit.4	32	B	CC.4.L.6
10	B	CC.4.Rlit.2	33	C	CC.4.Rinf.4
11	C	CC.4.Rlit.3	34	B	CC.4.Rinf.2
12	D	CC.4.L.5.b	35	C	CC.4.Rinf.1
13	A	CC.4.Rlit.1	36	D	CC.4.Rinf.2
14	D	CC.4.Rlit.4	37	A	CC.4.Rinf.3
15	D	CC.4.L.4.c	38	B	CC.4.Rinf.8
16	Rubric	CC.4.Rlit.6	39	D	CC.4.Rinf.5
17	B	CC.4.L.5.a	40	A	CC.4.L.4.a
18	B	CC.4.Rlit.1	41	C	CC.4.Rinf.4
19	C	CC.4.Rlit.2	42	Rubric	CC.4.Rinf.6
20	A	CC.4.L.5.a	43	D	CC.4.Rinf.2
21	C	CC.4.L.6	44	D	CC.4.Rinf.2
22	B	CC.4.Rlit.4	45	C	CC.4.Rinf.1
23	Rubric	CC.4.Rlit.5	46	A	CC.4.Rinf.8
			47	C	CC.4.Rinf.8
			48	B	CC.4.Rinf.5
			49	D	CC.4.Rinf.5
			50	A	CC.4.Rinf.4
			51	Rubric	CC.4.Rinf.9

Item 16 Rubric

Student writes a comparison that

3 points	fully describes the similarities and differences in the narrators' points of view in two stories.
2 points	partially describes the similarities and differences in the narrators' points of view in two stories.
1 point	is minimal and/or incorrect.

Item 23 Rubric

Student writes a comparison that

3 points	fully describes the differences between the structure and language of a poem and a story.
2 points	partially describes the differences between the structure and language of a poem and a story.
1 point	is minimal and/or incorrect.

Item 42 Rubric

Student writes a comparison that

3 points	fully describes how the first- or secondhand viewpoint affects the presentation of information in two passages on the same topic.
2 points	partially describes how the first- or secondhand viewpoint affects the presentation of information in two passages on the same topic.
1 point	is minimal and/or incorrect.

Item 51 Rubric

Student writes an explanation that

2 points	fully integrates information from two sources to correctly answer the question.
1 point	is partial and/or incorrect.

Scoring Note: Assign zero points if a student provides no response or an unscorable response.

Answer Keys and Rubrics
Benchmark Writing Test

Directions: Use the keys below to score the multiple-choice test items. Use the Skill Rubric on this page and the Writing Traits Rubric on page 104 to score student responses to writing prompts.

Benchmark Writing Test – Form B		
Item	**Key**	**Code**
1	D	CC.4.L.1.a
2	A	CC.4.L.1.d, W.5
3	A	CC.4.L.1.c
4	B	CC.4.L.1.g
5	A	CC.4.L.1.e
6	C	CC.4.L.2.b, W.5
7	A	CC.4.L.1.d, W.5
8	C	CC.4.L.1.b
9	B	CC.4.L.1.c
10	A	CC.4.L.1.f, W.5
11	D	CC.4.L.2.a, W.5
12	C	CC.4.L.2.c, W.5
13	Skill Rubric	CC.4.W.2.a, W.7, W.8, W.9.b
14	Skill Rubric	CC.4.W.2, W.4, W.5, W.7, W.8, W.9.b, L.1, L.2, L.3, L.6
15	Skill Rubric	CC.4.W.2, W.4, W.5, W.9.a, L.1, L.2, L.3, L.6
16	Skill Rubric	CC.4.W.1, W.4, W.5, L.1, L.2, L.3, L.6

Item 13 Skill Rubric	
Student writes a rough draft of a report that	
4 points	thoroughly incorporates the two research sources presented and makes use of notes and/or a graphic organizer.
3 points	adequately incorporates most of one or both research sources presented and makes use of notes and/or a graphic organizer.
2 points	makes some use of parts of one or both research sources presented and makes use of notes or a graphic organizer.
1 point	makes little if any use of any part of either research source presented or does not make use of any notes or a graphic organizer.

Scoring Note: Assign zero points if a student provides no response or an unscorable response.

Answer Keys and Rubrics
Benchmark Reading Test

Directions: Use the keys and rubrics below to score the test items.

Benchmark Reading Test – Form C						
Item	Key	Code	Item	Key	Code
1	B	CC.4.Rlit.1	26	A	CC.4.Rinf.2
2	C	CC.4.Rlit.3	27	B	CC.4.Rinf.8
3	B	CC.4.Rlit.1	28	C	CC.4.Rinf.8
4	D	CC.4.Rlit.2	29	D	CC.4.Rinf.2
5	D	CC.4.Rlit.3	30	C	CC.4.Rinf.3
6	C	CC.4.L.4.a	31	C	CC.4.Rinf.1
7	B	CC.4.Rlit.4	32	D	CC.4.Rinf.3
8	B	CC.4.L.5.a	33	B	CC.4.Rinf.5
9	C	CC.4.Rlit.3	34	B	CC.4.L.6
10	B	CC.4.Rlit.3	35	C	CC.4.Rinf.4
11	D	CC.4.Rlit.1	36	C	CC.4.Rinf.2
12	C	CC.4.Rlit.2	37	A	CC.4.Rinf.3
13	C	CC.4.Rlit.3	38	A	CC.4.Rinf.1
14	A	CC.4.L.4.b	39	B	CC.4.Rinf.2
15	C	CC.4.L.5.c	40	A	CC.4.Rinf.4
16	Rubric	CC.4.Rlit.7	41	D	CC.4.L.4.a
17	C	CC.4.Rlit.7	42	A	CC.4.L.4.b
18	B	CC.4.Rlit.1	43	Rubric	CC.4.Rinf.9
19	B	CC.4.L.5.b	44	C	CC.4.Rinf.2
20	C	CC.4.Rlit.1	45	A	CC.4.Rinf.3
21	D	CC.4.Rlit.2	46	C	CC.4.Rinf.1
22	C	CC.4.Rlit.3	47	D	CC.4.Rinf.2
23	B	CC.4.Rlit.4	48	D	CC.4.Rinf.5
24	B	CC.4.L.4.c	49	A	CC.4.Rinf.4
25	Rubric	CC.4.Rlit.9	50	B	CC.4.L.5.c
			51	C	CC.4.L.4.c
			52	Rubric	CC.4.Rinf.7

Item 16 Rubric

Student writes an explanation that

2 points	fully describes how the illustration contributes to understanding the story.
1 point	is partial and/or incorrect.

Item 25 Rubric

Student writes a comparison that

3 points	fully describes the similarities and differences of how the plots of two stories unfold.
2 points	partially describes the similarities and differences of how the plots of two stories unfold.
1 point	is minimal and/or incorrect.

Item 43 Rubric

Student writes a comparison that

3 points	fully describes the differences between the dangers faced by dolphins and seals in the two articles.
2 points	partially describes the differences between the dangers faced by dolphins and seals in the two articles.
1 point	is minimal and/or incorrect.

Item 52 Rubric

Student writes an explanation that

2 points	fully describes how the illustration is related to the article.
1 point	is partial and/or incorrect.

Scoring Note: Assign zero points if a student provides no response or an unscorable response.

Answer Keys and Rubrics
Benchmark Writing Test

Directions: Use the keys below to score the multiple-choice test items. Use the Skill Rubric on this page and the Writing Traits Rubric on page 104 to score student responses to writing prompts.

Benchmark Writing Test – Form C

Item	Key	Code
1	A	CC.4.L.1.c
2	C	CC.4.L.2.b, W.5
3	C	CC.4.L.1.g
4	B	CC.4.L.1.f, W.5
5	C	CC.4.L.1.e
6	D	CC.4.L.1.a
7	B	CC.4.L.1.b
8	A	CC.4.L.2.a, W.5
9	D	CC.4.L.1.e
10	C	CC.4.L.1.d, W.5
11	B	CC.4.L.2.c, W.5
12	B	CC.4.L.1.f, W.5
13	Skill Rubric	CC.4.W.2.a, W.7, W.8, W.9.b
14	Skill Rubric	CC.4.W.1, W.4, W.5, W.7, W.8, W.9.b, L.1, L.2, L.3, L.6
15	Skill Rubric	CC.4.W.3, W.4, W.5, L.1, L.2, L.3, L.6
16	Skill Rubric	CC.4.W.2, W.4, W.5, L.1, L.2, L.3, L.6

Item 13 Skill Rubric

Student writes a rough draft of a report that

4 points	thoroughly incorporates the two research sources presented and makes use of notes and/or a graphic organizer.
3 points	adequately incorporates most of one or both research sources presented and makes use of notes and/or a graphic organizer.
2 points	makes some use of parts of one or both research sources presented and makes use of notes or a graphic organizer.
1 point	makes little if any use of any part of either research source presented or does not make use of any notes or a graphic organizer.

Scoring Note: Assign zero points if a student provides no response or an unscorable response.

Writing Traits Rubric

Score Point	Topic and Support	Organization	Voice	Word Choice	Sentence Fluency	Conventions
4	• The writing has a clear topic and focused message that keeps readers interested. • Details are accurate and relevant, showing in-depth knowledge of the topic.	• The writing has a clear structure throughout that suits the writer's audience and purpose. • All content flows smoothly and logically.	• The writing sounds genuine and unique. • The writer's tone is appropriate to the purpose and audience.	• Effective words were chosen to clearly convey the writer's message. • Language used throughout is appropriate for the audience and grabs readers' attention.	• All sentences are varied and effective and have appropriate transitions. • When read aloud, the writing sounds natural and rhythmic.	• The writing has no more than a few minor errors in spelling, punctuation, capitalization, grammar, usage, and paragraphing. • All the sentences are complete.
3	• The writing has an adequate topic and message that keeps readers interested. • Most details are accurate and relevant, showing reasonable knowledge of the topic.	• The writing has an adequate structure that suits the writer's audience and purpose. • Most of the content flows smoothly and logically.	• Most of the writing sounds genuine and unique. • The writer's tone is mostly appropriate for the purpose and audience.	• Many appropriate words were chosen to clearly convey the writer's message. • Most language is appropriate for the audience and grabs readers' attention.	• Most sentences are varied and effective and have appropriate transitions. • When read aloud, most of the writing sounds natural and rhythmic.	• The writing has some errors in spelling, punctuation, capitalization, grammar, usage, and paragraphing. • Most of the sentences are complete.
2	• The writing has a somewhat unclear and unfocused topic and message, causing readers some confusion. • Some details are relevant and accurate, showing minimal knowledge of the topic.	• The writing has a vague structure that may suit the writer's audience and purpose. • Some content flows smoothly and logically.	• Some of the writing sounds genuine and unique. • The writer's tone is somewhat inappropriate for the purpose and audience.	• Some appropriate words were chosen to convey the writer's message. • Some language is appropriate for the audience and grabs readers' attention.	• Some sentences are varied and effective and have appropriate transitions. • When read aloud, some of the writing sounds natural and rhythmic.	• The writing has enough errors in spelling, punctuation, capitalization, grammar, usage, and paragraphing to necessitate rereading. • Some of the sentences are complete.
1	• The writing does not have a clear, focused topic or message, causing readers confusion. • Many details are irrelevant and/or inaccurate, indicating a lack of knowledge of the topic.	• The writing does not have a structure. • The content does not flow smoothly or logically.	• The writing does not sound genuine or unique. • The writer's tone is not appropriate for the purpose or audience.	• Few appropriate words were chosen to convey the writer's message. • Language is dull, vague, and inappropriate for the audience, losing the readers' attention.	• Few or none of the sentences are varied or effective or have appropriate transitions. • When read aloud, the writing sounds unnatural.	• The writing has many errors in spelling, punctuation, capitalization, grammar, usage, and paragraphing, impeding understanding. • Few sentences are complete.
0	Assign a score of zero for no response or an unscorable response.					

Student Profile
Benchmark Reading Tests

Name _____

Circle the item number for each item answered correctly. Assign 1 point for each correct answer. For items scored with a rubric, enter the student's score in the space provided. Calculate the total Reading Test score on the last page of this profile.

Code	Common Core State Standards — Reading Standards for Literature	Form A Item Numbers	Form A Points/Possible Points	Form B Item Numbers	Form B Points/Possible Points	Form C Item Numbers	Form C Points/Possible Points
		Date:		Date:		Date:	
CC.4.Rlit.1	Refer to details and examples in a text when explaining what the text says explicitly and when drawing inferences from the text. (RL.4.1)	3 5 9 12 19	___/5	1 2 13 18	___/4	1 3 11 18 20	___/5
CC.4.Rlit.2	Determine a theme of a story, drama, or poem from details in the text; summarize the text. (RL.4.2)	4 15 20	___/3	3 4 10 19	___/4	4 12 21	___/3
CC.4.Rlit.3	Describe in depth a character, setting, or event in a story or drama, drawing on specific details in the text (e.g., a character's thoughts, words, or actions). (RL.4.3)	1 2 10 13 14 18	___/6	5 6 11	___/3	2 5 9 10 13 22	___/6
CC.4.Rlit.4	Determine the meaning of words and phrases as they are used in a text, including those that allude to significant characters found in mythology (e.g., Herculean). (RL.4.4)	8 11 23	___/3	9 14 22	___/3	7 23	___/2
CC.4.Rlit.5	Explain major differences between poems, drama, and prose, and refer to the structural elements of poems (e.g., verse, rhythm, meter) and drama (e.g., casts of characters, settings, descriptions, dialogue, stage directions) when writing or speaking about a text. (RL.4.5)			23 (___/3)	___/3		
CC.4.Rlit.6	Compare and contrast the point of view from which different stories are narrated, including the difference between first- and third-person narrations. (RL.4.6)			16 (___/3)	___/3		
CC.4.Rlit.7	Make connections between the text of a story or drama and a visual or oral presentation of the text, identifying where each version reflects specific descriptions and directions in the text. (RL.4.7)					16 (___/2) 17	___/3
CC.4.Rlit.9	Compare and contrast the treatment of similar themes and topics (e.g., opposition of good and evil) and patterns of events (e.g., the quest) in stories, myths, and traditional literature from different cultures. (RL.4.9)	17 (___/3) 24 (___/3)	___/6			25 (___/3)	___/3
CC.4.Rlit.10	By the end of the year, read and comprehend literature, including stories, dramas, and poetry, in the grades 4–5 text complexity band proficiently, with scaffolding as needed at the high end of the range. (RL.4.10)	(included above)		(included above)		(included above)	
	Reading Literature Subtotal		___/23		___/20		___/22

Student Profile
Benchmark Reading Tests

Name _____

Code	Common Core State Standards — Reading Standards for Informational Text	Form A Item Numbers	Form A Points/Possible Points	Form B Item Numbers	Form B Points/Possible Points	Form C Item Numbers	Form C Points/Possible Points
		Date:		Date:		Date:	
CC.4.Rinf.1	Refer to details and examples in a text when explaining what the text says explicitly and when drawing inferences from the text. (RI.4.1)	27 34 48	___/3	25 35 45	___/3	31 38 46	___/3
CC.4.Rinf.2	Determine the main idea of a text and explain how it is supported by key details; summarize the text. (RI.4.2)	25 28 33 36 43 49	___/6	27 28 34 36 43 44	___/6	26 29 36 39 44 47	___/6
CC.4.Rinf.3	Explain events, procedures, ideas, or concepts in a historical, scientific, or technical text, including what happened and why, based on specific information in the text. (RI.4.3)	26 35 46	___/3	24 26 37	___/3	30 32 37 45	___/4
CC.4.Rinf.4	Determine the meaning of general academic and domain-specific words or phrases in a text relevant to a grade 4 topic or subject area. (RI.4.4)	31 39 40 47	___/4	33 41 50	___/3	35 40 49	___/3
CC.4.Rinf.5	Describe the overall structure (e.g., chronology, comparison, cause/effect, problem/solution) of events, ideas, concepts, or information in a text or part of a text. (RI.4.5)	29 38	___/2	29 39 48 49	___/4	33 48	___/2
CC.4.Rinf.6	Compare and contrast a firsthand and secondhand account of the same event or topic; describe the differences in focus and the information provided. (RI.4.6)	41 51 (___/3)	___/4	42 (___/3)	___/3		
CC.4.Rinf.7	Interpret information presented visually, orally, or quantitatively (e.g., in charts, graphs, diagrams, time lines, animations, or interactive elements on Web pages) and explain how the information contributes to an understanding of the text in which it appears. (RI.4.7)	32 (___/2)	___/2			52 (___/2)	___/2
CC.4.Rinf.8	Explain how an author uses reasons and evidence to support particular points in a text. (RI.4.8)	37 44	___/2	38 46 47	___/3	27 28	___/2
CC.4.Rinf.9	Integrate information from two texts on the same topic in order to write or speak about the subject knowledgeably. (RI.4.9)			51 (___/2)	___/2	43 (___/3)	___/3
CC.4.Rinf.10	By the end of year, read and comprehend informational texts, including history/social studies, science, and technical texts, in the grades 4-5 text complexity band proficiently, with scaffolding as needed at the high end of the range. (RI.4.10)	(included above)		(included above)		(included above)	
	Reading Informational Text Subtotal		___/26		___/27		___/25

Student Profile
Benchmark Reading Tests

Name _____

Code	Common Core State Standards	Form A Item Numbers	Form A Points/Possible Points	Form B Item Numbers	Form B Points/Possible Points	Form C Item Numbers	Form C Points/Possible Points
		Date:		Date:		Date:	
	Language Standards (included in the Reading Test)						
CC.4.L.4	Determine or clarify the meaning of unknown and multiple-meaning words and phrases based on *grade 4 reading and content, choosing flexibly from a range of strategies*. (L.4.4)						
	a. Use context (e.g., definitions, examples, or restatements in text) as a clue to the meaning of a word or phrase. (L.4.4a)	7 30	___ /2	8 40	___ /2	6 41	___ /2
	b. Use common, grade-appropriate Greek and Latin affixes and roots as clues to the meaning of a word (e.g., *telegraph, photograph, autograph*). (L.4.4b)	45	___ /1	31	___ /1	14 42	___ /2
	c. Consult reference materials (e.g., dictionaries, glossaries, thesauruses), both print and digital, to find the pronunciation and determine or clarify the precise meaning of key words and phrases. (L.4.4c)	42 50	___ /2	15	___ /1	24 51	___ /2
CC.4.L.5	Demonstrate understanding of figurative language, word relationships, and nuances in word meanings. (L.4.5)						
	a. Explain the meaning of simple similes and metaphors (e.g., *as pretty as a picture*) in context. (L.4.5a)	6	___ /1	17 20	___ /2	8	___ /1
	b. Recognize and explain the meaning of common idioms, adages, and proverbs. (L.4.5b)	21	___ /1	12	___ /1	19	___ /1
	c. Demonstrate understanding of words by relating them to their opposites (antonyms) and to words with similar but not identical meanings (synonyms). (L.4.5c)	16	___ /1	7 30	___ /2	15 50	___ /2
CC.4.L.6	Acquire and use accurately grade-appropriate general academic and domain-specific words and phrases, including those that signal precise actions, emotions, or states of being (e.g., *quizzed, whined, stammered* and that are basic to a particular topic (e.g., *wildlife, conservation,* and *endangered* when discussing animal preservation). (L.4.6)	22	___ /1	21 32	___ /2	34	___ /2
	Language (included in Reading Test) Subtotal		___ /9		___ /11		___ /11

Benchmark Reading Test Total Score	Form A	/58	Form B	/58	Form C	/58
	___		___		___	

To calculate the Benchmark Reading Test Total Score, add Subtotal scores for Reading Literature, Reading Informational Text, and Language.

107

Benchmark Test

Name _____

Student Profile
Benchmark Writing Tests

Use the Answer Keys and Rubrics to score items 1–13. Use the Writing Traits Rubric to score items 14–16. Circle the item number for each item answered correctly. Assign 1 point for each correct answer. For items scored with a rubric, enter the student's score in the space provided. Calculate the total Writing Test score on the next page of this profile.

Code	Common Core State Standards / Language Standards	Form A Date: Item Numbers	Form A Points/Possible Points	Form B Date: Item Numbers	Form B Points/Possible Points	Form C Date: Item Numbers	Form C Points/Possible Points
CC.4.L.1	Demonstrate command of the conventions of standard English grammar and usage when writing or speaking. (L.4.1)						
	a. Use relative pronouns (*who, whose, whom, which, that*) and relative adverbs (*where, when, why*). (L.4.1a)	1 7	___/2	1	___/1	6	___/1
	b. Form and use the progressive (e.g., *I was walking; I am walking; I will be walking*) verb tenses. (L.4.1b)	2 9	___/2	8	___/1	7	___/1
	c. Use modal auxiliaries (e.g., *can, may, must*) to convey various conditions. (L.4.1c)	3	___/1	3 9	___/2	1	___/1
	d. Order adjectives within sentences according to conventional patterns (e.g., *a small red bag* rather than *a red small bag*). (L.4.1d)	10	___/1	2 7	___/2	10	___/2
	e. Form and use prepositional phrases. (L.4.1e)	4	___/1	5	___/1	5 9	___/2
	f. Produce complete sentences, recognizing and correcting inappropriate fragments and run-ons. (L.4.1f)	12	___/1	10	___/1	4 12	___/2
	g. Correctly use frequently confused words (e.g., *to, too, two; there, their*). (L.4.1g)	6	___/1	4	___/1	3	___/1
CC.4.L.2	Demonstrate command of the conventions of standard English capitalization, punctuation, and spelling when writing. (L.4.2)						
	a. Use correct capitalization. (L.4.2a)	11	___/1	11	___/1	8	___/1
	b. Use commas and quotation marks to mark direct speech and quotations from a text. (L.4.2b)	5	___/1	6	___/1	2	___/1
	c. Use a comma before a coordinating conjunction in a compound sentence. (L.4.2c)	8	___/1	12	___/1	11	___/1
	d. Spell grade-appropriate words correctly, consulting references as needed. (L.4.2d)						
	Language (included in the Writing Test) Subtotal		___/12		___/12		___/12

Student Profile
Benchmark Writing Tests

Name _____

Common Core State Standards	Form A		Form B		Form C	
	Date:		Date:		Date:	
Writing Standards	Item Numbers	Points/Possible Points	Item Numbers	Points/Possible Points	Item Numbers	Points/Possible Points
For item 13, use the Skill Rubric on the Answer Keys and Rubrics pages to score student's response. The codes for the Common Core State Standards that align with this item are listed on the Answer Keys and Rubrics pages.	13	___ /4	13	___ /4	13	___ /4
For items 14-16, use the Writing Traits Rubric to score student's responses. You can record student's scores by trait on the next two pages. The codes for the Common Core State Standards that align with these items are listed on the Answer Keys and Rubrics pages.	14	___ /24	14	___ /24	14	___ /24
	15	___ /24	15	___ /24	15	___ /24
	16	___ /24	16	___ /24	16	___ /24
Writing Subtotal		___ /76		___ /76		___ /76

Benchmark Writing Test Total Score	Form A	Form B	Form C
	___ /88	___ /88	___ /88

To calculate the Benchmark Writing Test Total Score, add Subtotal scores for Language and Writing.

Student Profile
Benchmark Writing Tests

For the item numbers below, use the Writing Traits Rubric to score the student's responses. Then enter the student's trait scores below and calculate the total points. Record the total points for each item on the second page of the Student Profile.

Form A

Item 14	Topic and Support CC.4.W.2, W.4, W.5, W.7, W.8, W.9.b	Organization CC.4.W.2.a, W.2.e, W.4, W.5	Voice CC.4.L.3, W.4, W.5	Word Choice CC.4.L.3, L.6, W.2.c, W.2.d, W.4, W.5	Sentence Fluency CC.4.L.1.f, L.3, W.2.c, W.4, W.5	Conventions CC.4.L.1, L.2, W.5	Total Points
	_____/4	_____/4	_____/4	_____/4	_____/4	_____/4	_____/24

Item 15	Topic and Support CC.4.W.3, W.4, W.5	Organization CC.4.W.3.a, W.3.e, W.4, W.5	Voice CC.4.L.3, W.3.b, W.4, W.5	Word Choice CC.4.L.3, L.6, W.3.c, W.3.d, W.4, W.5	Sentence Fluency CC.4.L.1.f, L.3, W.3.c, W.4, W.5	Conventions CC.4.L.1, L.2, W.5	Total Points
	_____/4	_____/4	_____/4	_____/4	_____/4	_____/4	_____/24

Item 16	Topic and Support CC.4.W.1, W.4, W.5	Organization CC.4.W.1.a, W.1.d, W.4, W.5	Voice CC.4.L.3, W.4, W.5	Word Choice CC.4.L.3, L.6, W.1.c, W.4, W.5	Sentence Fluency CC.4.L.1.f, L.3, W.1.c, W.4, W.5	Conventions CC.4.L.1, L.2, W.5	Total Points
	_____/4	_____/4	_____/4	_____/4	_____/4	_____/4	_____/24

Form B

Item 14	Topic and Support CC.4.W.2, W.4, W.5, W.7, W.8, W.9.b	Organization CC.4.W.2.a, W.2.e, W.4, W.5	Voice CC.4.L.3, W.4, W.5	Word Choice CC.4.L.3, L.6, W.2.c, W.2.d, W.4, W.5	Sentence Fluency CC.4.L.1.f, L.3, W.2.c, W.4, W.5	Conventions CC.4.L.1, L.2, W.5	Total Points
	_____/4	_____/4	_____/4	_____/4	_____/4	_____/4	_____/24

Item 15	Topic and Support CC.4.W.2, W.4, W.5, W.9.a	Organization CC.4.W.2.a, W.2.e, W.4, W.5	Voice CC.4.L.3, W.4, W.5	Word Choice CC.4.L.3, L.6, W.2.c, W.2.d, W.4, W.5	Sentence Fluency CC.4.L.1.f, L.3, W.2.c, W.4, W.5	Conventions CC.4.L.1, L.2, W.5	Total Points
	_____/4	_____/4	_____/4	_____/4	_____/4	_____/4	_____/24

Continued on next page

Name _____

Student Profile
Benchmark Writing Tests

Item 16	Topic and Support	Organization	Voice	Word Choice	Sentence Fluency	Conventions	Total Points
	CC.4.W.1, W.4, W.5	CC.4.W.1.a, W.1.d, W.4, W.5	CC.4.L.3, W.4, W.5	CC.4.L.3, L.6, W.1.c, W.4, W.5	CC.4.L.1.f, L.3, W.1.c, W.4, W.5	CC.4.L.1, L.2, W.5	
	_____ / 4	_____ / 4	_____ / 4	_____ / 4	_____ / 4	_____ / 4	_____ /24

Form C

Item 14	Topic and Support	Organization	Voice	Word Choice	Sentence Fluency	Conventions	Total Points
	CC.4.W.1, W.4, W.5, W.7, W.8, W.9.b	CC.4.W.1.a, W.1.e, W.4, W.5	CC.4.L.3, W.4, W.5	CC.4.L.3, L.6, W.1.c, W.1.d, W.4, W.5	CC.4.L.1.f, L.3, W.1.c, W.4, W.5	CC.4.L.1, L.2, W.5	
	_____ / 4	_____ / 4	_____ / 4	_____ / 4	_____ / 4	_____ / 4	_____ /24

Item 15	Topic and Support	Organization	Voice	Word Choice	Sentence Fluency	Conventions	Total Points
	CC.4.W.3, W.4, W.5	CC.4.W.3.a, W.3.e, W.4, W.5	CC.4.L.3, W.3.b, W.4, W.5	CC.4.L.3, L.6, W.3.c, W.3.d, W.4, W.5	CC.4.L.1.f, L.3, W.3.c, W.4, W.5	CC.4.L.1, L.2, W.5	
	_____ / 4	_____ / 4	_____ / 4	_____ / 4	_____ / 4	_____ / 4	_____ /24

Item 16	Topic and Support	Organization	Voice	Word Choice	Sentence Fluency	Conventions	Total Points
	CC.4.W.2, W.4, W.5	CC.4.W.2.a, W.2.d, W.4, W.5	CC.4.L.3, W.4, W.5	CC.4.L.3, L.6, W.2.c, W.4, W.5	CC.4.L.1.f, L.3, W.2.c, W.4, W.5	CC.4.L.1, L.2, W.5	
	_____ / 4	_____ / 4	_____ / 4	_____ / 4	_____ / 4	_____ / 4	_____ /24

Class Grouping Summary
Benchmark Reading Tests

Circle the form of the Benchmark Reading Test that you administered. Next to each Common Core State Standard, write the names or initials of students who would benefit from more instruction or practice on tasks related to the Standard.

Common Core State Standards		Form: A B C
Code	Reading Standards for Literature	Date:
CC.4.Rlit.1	Refer to details and examples in a text when explaining what the text says explicitly and when drawing inferences from the text. (RL.4.1)	
CC.4.Rlit.2	Determine a theme of a story, drama, or poem from details in the text; summarize the text. (RL.4.2)	
CC.4.Rlit.3	Describe in depth a character, setting, or event in a story or drama, drawing on specific details in the text (e.g., a character's thoughts, words, or actions.) (RL.4.3)	
CC.4.Rlit.4	Determine the meaning of words and phrases as they are used in a text, including those that allude to significant characters found in mythology (e.g., Herculean). (RL.4.4)	
CC.4.Rlit.5	Explain major differences between poems, drama, and prose, and refer to the structural elements of poems (e.g., verse, rhythm, meter) and drama (e.g., casts of characters, settings, descriptions, dialogue, stage directions) when writing or speaking about a text. (RL.4.5)	
CC.4.Rlit.6	Compare and contrast the point of view from which different stories are narrated, including the difference between first- and third-person narrations. (RL.4.6)	
CC.4.Rlit.7	Make connections between the text of a story or drama and a visual or oral presentation of the text, identifying where each version reflects specific descriptions and directions in the text. (RL.4.7)	
CC.4.Rlit.9	Compare and contrast the treatment of similar themes and topics (e.g., opposition of good and evil) and patterns of events (e.g., the quest) in stories, myths, and traditional literature from different cultures. (RL.4.9)	
CC.4.Rlit.10	By the end of the year, read and comprehend literature, including stories, dramas, and poetry, in the grades 4-5 text complexity band proficiently with scaffolding as needed at the high end of the range. (RL.4.10)	

Class Grouping Summary
Benchmark Reading Tests

Circle the form of the Benchmark Reading Test that you administered. Next to each Common Core State Standard, write the names or initials of students who would benefit from more instruction or practice on tasks related to the Standard.

Common Core State Standards		Form: A B C		
Code	**Reading Standards for Informational Text**	Date:		
CC.4.Rinf.1	Refer to details and examples in a text when explaining what the text says explicitly and when drawing inferences from the text. (RI.4.1)			
CC.4.Rinf.2	Determine the main idea of a text and explain how it is supported by key details; summarize the text. (RI.4.2)			
CC.4.Rinf.3	Explain events, procedures, ideas, or concepts in a historical, scientific, or techinical text, including what happened and why, based on specific information in the text. (RI.4.3)			
CC.4.Rinf.4	Determine the meaning of general academic and domain-specific words or phrases in a text relevant to *a grade 4 topic or subject area.* (RI.4.4)			
CC.4.Rinf.5	Describe the overall structure (e.g., chronology, comparison, cause/effect, problem/solution) of events, ideas, concepts, or information in a text or part of a text. (RI.4.5)			
CC.4.Rinf.6	Compare and contrast a firsthand and secondhand account of the same event or topic; describe the differences in focus and the information provided. (RI.4.6)			
CC.4.Rinf.7	Interpret information presented visually, orally, or quantitatively (e.g., in charts, graphs, diagrams, time lines, animations, or interactive elements on Web pages) and explain how the information contributes to an understanding of the text in which it appears. (RI.4.7)			
CC.4.Rinf.8	Explain how an author uses reasons and evidence to support particular points in a text. (RI.4.8)			
CC.4.Rinf.9	Integrate information from two texts on the same topic in order to write or speak about the subject knowledgeably. (RI.4.9)			
CC.4.Rinf.10	By the end of year, read and comprehend informational texts, including history/social studies, science, and technical texts, in the grades 4-5 text complexity band proficiently, with scaffolding as needed at the high end of the range. (RI.4.10)			

Class Grouping Summary
Benchmark Reading Tests

Circle the form of the Benchmark Reading Test that you administered. Next to each Common Core State Standard, write the names or initials of students who would benefit from more instruction or practice on tasks related to the Standard.

Common Core State Standards		Form: A B C
Code	**Language Standards for Reading**	**Date:**
CC.4.L.4	Determine or clarify the meaning of unknown and multiple-meaning words and phrases based on *grade 4 reading and content*, choosing flexibly from a range of strategies. (L.4.4)	
	a. Use context (e.g., definitions, examples, or restatements in text) as a clue to the meaning of a word or phrase. (L.4.4a)	
	b. Use common, grade-appropriate Greek and Latin affixes and roots as clues to the meaning of a word (e.g., *telegraph, photograph, autograph*). (L.4.4b)	
	c. Consult reference materials (e.g., dictionaries, glossaries, thesauruses), both print and digital, to find the pronunciation and determine or clarify the precise meaning of key words and phrases. (L.4.4c)	
CC.4.L.5	Demonstrate understanding of figurative language, word relationships, and nuances in word meanings. (L.4.5)	
	a. Explain the meaning of simple similes and metaphors (e.g., *as pretty as a picture*) in context. (L.4.5a)	
	b. Recognize and explain the meaning of common idioms, adages, and proverbs. (L.4.5b)	
	c. Demonstrate understanding of words by relating them to their opposites (antonyms) and to words with similar but not identical meanings (synonyms). (L.4.5c)	
CC.4.L.6	Acquire and use accurately grade-appropriate general academic and domain-specific words and phrases, including those that signal precise actions, emotions, or states of being (e.g., *quizzed, whined, stammered*) and that are basic to a particular topic (e.g., *wildlife, conservation,* and *endangered* when discussing animal preservation). (L.4.6)	

Class Grouping Summary
Benchmark Writing Tests

Circle the form of the Benchmark Writing Test that you administered. Next to each Common Core State Standard, write the names or initials of students who would benefit from more instruction or practice on tasks related to the Standard.

Common Core State Standards		Form: A B C
Code	**Writing Standards**	**Date:**
CC.4.W.1	Write opinion pieces on topics and texts, supporting a point of view with reasons and information. (W.4.1)	
CC.4.W.2	Write informative/explanatory texts to examine a topic and convey ideas and information clearly. (W.4.2)	
CC.4.W.3	Write narratives to develop real or imagined experiences or events using effective technique, descriptive details, and clear event sequences. (W.4.3)	
CC.4.W.4	Produce clear and coherent writing in which the development and organization are appropriate to task, purpose, and audience. (Grade-specific expectations for writing types are defined in standards 1-3 above.) (W.4.4)	
CC.4.W.5	With guidance and support from peers and adults, develop and strengthen writing as needed by planning, revising, and editing. (Editing for conventions should demonstrate command of Language standards 1-3 up to and including grade 4.) (W.4.5)	
CC.4.W.7	Conduct short research projects that build knowledge through investigation of different aspects of a topic. (W.4.7)	
CC.4.W.8	Recall relevant information from experiences or gather relevant information from print and digital sources; take notes and categorize information, and provide a list of sources. (W.4.8)	
CC.4.W.9	Draw evidence from literary or informational texts to support analysis, reflection, and research. (W.4.9)	
	a. Apply *grade 4 Reading standards* to literature (e.g., "Describe in depth a character, setting, or event in a story or drama, drawing on specific details in the text [e.g., a character's thoughts, words, or actions]."). (W.4.9a)	
	b. Apply *grade 4 Reading standards* to informational texts (e.g., "Explain how an author uses reasons and evidence to support particular points in a text"). (W.4.9b)	

Class Grouping Summary
Benchmark Writing Tests

Circle the form of the Benchmark Writing Test that you administered. Next to each Common Core State Standard, write the names or initials of students who would benefit from more instruction or practice on tasks related to the Standard.

Common Core State Standards		Form: A B C
Code	**Language Standards for Writing**	**Date:**
CC.4.L.1	Demonstrate command of the conventions of standard English grammar and usage when writing or speaking. (L.4.1)	
	a. Use relative pronouns (*who, whose, whom, which, that*) and relative adverbs (*where, when, why*). (L.4.1a)	
	b. Form and use the progressive (e.g., *I was walking; I am walking; I will be walking*) verb tenses. (L.4.1b)	
	c. Use modal auxiliaries (e.g., *can, may, must*) to convey various conditions. (L.4.1c)	
	d. Order adjectives within sentences according to conventional patterns (e.g., *a small red bag* rather than *a red small bag*). (L.4.1d)	
	e. Form and use prepositional phrases. (L.4.1e)	
	f. Produce complete sentences, recognizing and correcting inappropriate fragments and run-ons. (L.4.1f)	
	g. Correctly use frequently confused words (e.g., *to, too, two; there, their*). (L.4.1g)	
CC.4.L.2	Demonstrate command of the conventions of standard English capitalization, punctuation, and spelling when writing. (L.4.2)	
	a. Use correct capitalization. (L.4.2a)	
	b. Use commas and quotation marks to mark direct speech and quotations from a text. (L.4.2b)	
	c. Use a comma before a coordinating conjunction in a compound sentence. (L.4.2c)	
	d. Spell grade-appropriate words correctly, consulting references as needed. (L.4.2d)	
CC.4.L.3	Use knowledge of language and its conventions when writing, speaking, reading, or listening. (L.4.3)	
	a. Choose words and phrases to convey ideas precisely. (L.4.3a)	
	b. Choose punctuation for effect. (L.4.3b)	
	c. Differentiate between contexts that call for formal English (e.g., presenting ideas) and situations where informal discourse is appropriate (e.g., small-group discussion). (L.4.3c)	